ACCESS TO 200+ SARASOTA RESTAURANT MENUS

The Little Sarasota DINING Book.

dS
dineSARASOTA

2022

UPDATED CARRYOUT & DELIVERY INFO

DINESARASOTA.COM

The Little Sarasota DINING Book.
13th Edition | 2022

To contact us, please send email to:
press@dinesarasota.com

Printed in the USA

10 9 8 7 6 5 4 3 2 1

ISBN 978-0-9862840-7-6

THANK YOU!

Thanks for picking up the 13th edition of our annual Sarasota dining book. We just love to be able to bring you Sarasota restaurant information in a format that you can use every day. But like most things in life, we couldn't do it without help.

Thanks to Knickole Barger, Robert Castellon, Ashley Chambers, Allison Chavez, Ciera Coleman, Isaac Correa, Nita Ettinger, Judi Gallagher, J.R. Garraus, Michael Klauber, Natalia Levey, Ken Lumpkin, Juliana Montane, and Ed Paulsen for contributing to this year's edition. It is fantastic to have such talented people in our community. And we're grateful for their help.

Lauren Ettinger (print) and Jen Hogan (digital) make sure it's actually possible for you to read all things we write about. Thank you for your editing skills and masterful use of the red pen.

A special thanks to Harrison Hoffman and Annabeth Carroll. I was really on the fence whether to publish a dining book last year (2021) or not. I'm glad they pushed me to do it. Doing last years edition made this year's version that much easier and better.

As always, thanks to you! Thank you for supporting what we do. We're always striving to make sure that our local Sarasota restaurants get the attention they so richly deserve. I know that they appreciate you too!

It's been a busy year here at dineSarasota. We sold a record amount of our 2021 dining books. If you purchased one, thank you SO much! We love being able to bring you restaurant information that can make your local dining decisions just a touch easier.

2021 brought some big changes to the way we provide Sarasota restaurant content digitally. Of course, there is still the dineSarasota.com database of restaurant information. Thanks for using that. But now there's lots more.

This past summer, we were selected by Facebook to be among the first to contribute content to their new independent writing platform, Bulletin. In August we launched our Bulletin newsletter, **Sarasota Bites**. If you have already subscribed, we appreciate it. If you haven't, we have provided you with a special QR code at the bottom of page 119. Just scan with your mobile device and you'll be on your way to all the latest food happenings in Sarasota.

Sometime in the coming year we will be launching a special, members only section of our Bulletin newsletter that will have a lot of great bonus content, perks, and restaurant info. Keep an eye out for that, it's going to be fun!

We're happy that our Sarasota restaurant community has bounced back so strong from all the issues caused by the COVID pandemic. Staffing shortages, supply chain issues, and a sea of new regulations made for a very difficult operating environment for our local restaurants. But they proved once again why they are some of the best in the country! It's a big part of what makes Sarasota so special.

Larry Hoffman
Publisher, dineSarasota.com

2022 DINESARASOTA TOP 50

- ☐ 1   GROVE Restaurant
- ☐ 2   Mattison's Forty One
- ☐ 3   Pier 22
- ☐ 4   Drunken Poet Cafe
- ☐ 5   Michael's on East
- ☐ 6   Sage
- ☐ 7   Duval's Fresh. Local. Seafood.
- ☐ 8   Café L'Europe
- ☐ 9   Bijou Cafe
- ☐ 10   Capital Grille
- ☐ 11   The Columbia Restaurant
- ☐ 12   Walt's Fish Market
- ☐ 13   The Old Salty Dog
- ☐ 14   Siesta Key Oyster Bar
- ☐ 15   Kiyoshi's Sushi
- ☐ 16   Harry's Continental Kitchens
- ☐ 17   Casey Key Fish House
- ☐ 18   Dim Sum King
- ☐ 19   Old Salty Dog
- ☐ 20   The Whiskey Barrel*
- ☐ 21   The Lily Cafe*
- ☐ 22   Munchies 420 Café
- ☐ 23   Tripletail Seafood & Spirits*
- ☐ 24   Karl Ehmer's Alpine Steak House
- ☐ 25   Phillippi Creek Oyster Bar
- ☐ 26   Yoder's Restaurant
- ☐ 27   Island House Tap & Grill
- ☐ 28   Cafe Barbosso
- ☐ 29   Jpan Restaurant

HOW TO USE THIS CHECKLIST - Like you really need an explanation for this. But, just in case, here goes. Get out there and eat through our Top 50! We've made it easy for you to keep track of your culinary adventures. These are the restaurants that you've been searching for, clicking on, and downloading on our dineSarasota.com website all year. So, in a way this is really *your* Top 50. And, if you flip to the back of this book, we've left a couple of note pages for you to keep track of your favorites. Go ahead, start your own Sarasota restaurant journal.

* Opened since our last edition.

HOW TO USE THIS BOOK

Thanks for picking up a copy of the latest *Little Sarasota DINING Book*. We're hoping that you're going to use it as your go-to guide to Sarasota dining. Now that you're the proud owner of a copy, we're going to give you some helpful inside tips on how to use the guide.

First off, it's arranged alphabetically. So, if you know the alphabet, you can use our guide. Yes, it's really that easy. It has basic restaurant information in each listing. Name, address, phone… also lists the restaurant's website if you would like to go there for additional information.

In the outlined bar, it will tell you the neighborhood/area that the restaurant is located in, the cuisine it serves, and its relative expense. It's relative to Sarasota, not NYC, keep that in mind.

The hours of operation are also listed. It's nice to know when they are open. We try our best to make this info as accurate as possible. But sometimes, Sarasota restaurants have special seasonal hours. Even though the COVID situation has gotten better, things have a tendency to change. If there's a question, it's best to call the restaurant.

For each place we'll also tell you what you can expect. Is it noisy or quiet? Good for kids? Maybe a late night menu. It's not an exhaustive list, just some of the highlights to guide your dining decision making process.

There aren't a lot of mysterious symbols that you have to reference. If you see this *, it means the restaurant has more than one location. We've listed what we consider to be the main one. The other locations are usually listed in the super handy cross reference in the back of the book.

Speaking of the cross reference, here's the scoop. Restaurants are listed in alphabetical order (you're good at that now!). We give you basic info. Name, address, phone. Restaurants are then listed by cuisine type and then by location. So, you can easily find that perfect seafood restaurant on Longboat Key.

QR CODES. If you'll notice, each restaurant listing has a little square box with a bunch of jumbled up dots. That's your easy access to the restaurants menu. Just scan that little code with the QR reader on your smartphone and just like magic, there's the menu! Pretty great, right? Oh, what if I don't have a smartphone? Well, then it might be time for an upgrade!

OK. Here's where things really get interesting. You now know where things are located and what type of food you can expect. But, let's dive in a little deeper. Let's say you're just visiting beautiful, sunny Sarasota AND you've got kids. What would be a good choice? How about celebrating a special occasion or event? Or, maybe you would just like to eat a meal and gaze longingly upon our blue waters. Where's the best spot?

That's where our specialty categories come in. Here are some things to keep in mind. First, we've curated these restaurant lists just for you. Second, these places may not be the only ones in town that fit the description. But, we think they're among the best. Hey, why isn't my favorite pizza place on that list? We're not trying to snub anybody here, but, there's only so much space.

LIVE MUSIC – Really self-explanatory. But, the music ranges from piano bar to acoustic guitar to rock 'n' roll. So, you may want to see who's playing the night you're going. Also, yes, there are other places in town that have live music.

CATERING – You could probably convince most restaurants to cater your twelve person dinner or throw together some to-go food for you to arrange on your own platters. The places listed here do it for REAL. They cater regularly.

EASY ON YOUR WALLET – A little perspective is in order here. Nothing on this list comes close to the McDonald's Dollar Menu (thankfully). That being said, these are some places you could go and not dip into your kids 529 plan to pay the bill. Something to keep in mind, "Easy on the wallet" depends a little on how big your billfold is. These restaurants won't break the budget.

NEW – No explanation necessary. These restaurants are "relatively" new. Some have been open longer than others. But, they've opened since our last edition.

SPORTS + FOOD + FUN – If the big game is on and you want to see it. Here are some places that do that well. Lots of places have a TV in the bar. These go above and beyond that.

GREAT BURGERS – Nothing evokes a more passionate outcry of food worship than a good burger debate. The truth is, we don't want to do that. But, this will probably start a conversation at a minimum. Again, lots of spots serve burgers. In our opinion, these standout.

NICE WINE LIST – Hmmm… A 2006 Cabernet or a 2015 Pouilly-Fuissé? That is one tough question. No "wine in a box" here. These restaurants all have a sturdy wine list and are proud of it. If you can be a little intimidated with the task of choosing a wine, relax. These spots usually have someone to hold your hand and walk you through it.

A BEAUTIFUL WATER VIEW – Nothing says Florida like a picture perfect view of the water. And, these places have that. The food runs the gamut from bar food to fine dining.

LATER NIGHT MENU – This is not New York, it is not Miami or Chicago either. That is the context with which you should navigate this list. Notice we said "LATER" night menu and NOT "late night menu." We're a reasonably early dining town. The places listed here are open past the time when half of Sarasota is safely tucked in bed. They all might not be 1AM, but, we do have a 4:20AMer in there!

SARASOTA FINE DINING – It's not great when people look down their nose at our upscale dining scene. We have some damn good chefs here in Sarasota. And, they're showing off their skills every single day. They should be celebrated. This list may not contain Le Bernardin, Alinea, or The French Laundry. But, we have some REAL contenders.

Lastly, there is always the question, "How do these restaurants get into this book?" They are selected based on their yearly popularity on dineSarasota.com. These are the restaurants that YOU are interested in. You've been searching for them on our website all year long. There are no advertisements here. So, that being said, you can't buy your way in. It's all you. This is really YOUR guide. And, I must say you have great taste!

A SPRIG OF THYME
1962 Hillview Street
941-330-8890
asprigofthymesrq.com

SOUTHSIDE VILLAGE	EUROPEAN	COST: $$

HOURS: Tues-Sat, 5PM to 9PM
CLOSED SUNDAY & MONDAY (SUMMER ONLY)

WHAT TO EXPECT: Upscale, casual • Good for a date
European bistro feel • Good wine list

CARRYOUT/DELIVERY INFO: Full menu available for carryout.
Curbside and contactless pick up. Delivery not available.

SCAN FOR MENU

SOME BASICS
Reservations:	YES
Spirits:	BEER/WINE
Parking:	STREET
Outdoor Dining:	YES

ALMAZONICA CERVECERIA `NEW`
4141 South Tamiami Trail
941-260-5964
almazonicacerveceria.com

SOUTH TRAIL	PERUVIAN	COST: $$

HOURS: Tues-Sat, 4PM to 10PM
CLOSED SUNDAY & MONDAY

WHAT TO EXPECT: Upscale • Small Batch Cerveceria
Chef Darwin's ceviche! • Lots of parking

CARRYOUT/DELIVERY INFO: Full menu available for carryout.
Curbside and contactless pick up. Delivery not available.

SCAN FOR MENU

SOME BASICS
Reservations:	YES
Spirits:	BEER/WINE
Parking:	LOT
Outdoor Dining:	NO

AMORE RESTAURANT
180 North Lime Avenue
941-383-1111
amorelbk.com

ITALIAN	COST: $$$

HOURS: Wed-Sun, 5PM to 9PM
CLOSED MONDAY & TUESDAY

WHAT TO EXPECT: OpenTable reservations • Upscale Italian
Casual, relaxed atmosphere • Also a Portuguese menu

CARRYOUT/DELIVERY INFO: Most menu items available for
carryout and delivery. Contactless & curbside pick up available.
Delivery available through Slice.

SCAN FOR MENU

SOME BASICS
Reservations:	YES
Spirits:	BEER/WINE
Parking:	LOT
Outdoor Dining:	NO

ANDREA'S
2085 Siesta Drive
941-951-9200
andreasrestaurantsrq.com

SOUTHGATE	ITALIAN	COST: $$$

HOURS: Mon-Sat, 5PM to 10PM
CLOSED SUNDAY (summer only)

WHAT TO EXPECT: Nice wine list • Quiet restaurant atmosphere
Upscale Italian cuisine • Great special occasion place

CARRYOUT/DELIVERY INFO: Special menu for carryout and
delivery. Contactless & curbside pick up available. Phone-in only.
Delivery not available. Cash or check for delivery.

SCAN FOR MENU

SOME BASICS
Reservations:	YES
Spirits:	BEER/WINE
Parking:	LOT
Outdoor Dining:	NO

ANNA MARIA OYSTER BAR

6906 14th Street W.*
941-758-7880
oysterbar.net

BRADENTON	SEAFOOD	COST: $$

HOURS: Sun-Thur, 11AM to 9PM • Fri-Sat, 11AM to 10PM

WHAT TO EXPECT: Good for kids • Casual, family atmosphere
Large menu • Good for groups

CARRYOUT/DELIVERY INFO: Full menu carryout available.
Phone-in ordering. Curbside pick up. Special menu for delivery.
Service through Uber Eats, Grubhub and DoorDash.

SCAN FOR MENU

SOME BASICS
Reservations:	8 OR MORE
Spirits:	FULL BAR
Parking:	LOT
Outdoor Dining:	YES

ANNA'S DELI

6535 Midnight Pass Road
941-349-4888
annasdelis.com

SIESTA KEY	DELI	COST: $

HOURS: Daily, 10:30AM to 4PM

WHAT TO EXPECT: Super casual • Great sandwiches (The Surfer)
Good for SK beach to go • Super fast service

CARRYOUT/DELIVERY INFO: Full menu available for carry out.
Delivery not available.

SCAN FOR MENU

SOME BASICS
Reservations:	NO
Spirits:	NONE
Parking:	LOT
Outdoor Dining:	NO

APOLLONIA GRILL

8235 Cooper Creek Boulevard*
941-359-4816
apolloniagrill.com

UPARK	GREEK	COST: $$

HOURS: Mon-Thur, 11:30AM to 9PM • Fri & Sat, 11:30AM to 10PM
Sunday, 11:30AM to 8:30PM

WHAT TO EXPECT: Good for groups • Family owned
Casual dining • Lots of parking • Also a Landings location

CARRYOUT/DELIVERY INFO: Most menu items available for
carryout and delivery. Curbside and contactless pick up.
Delivery available through DoorDash.

SCAN FOR MENU

SOME BASICS
Reservations:	YES
Spirits:	FULL BAR
Parking:	LOT
Outdoor Dining:	YES

ATHEN'S FAMILY RESTAURANT

2300 Bee Ridge Road
941-706-4121
athensfamilyrestaurant.business.site

	GREEK	COST: $$

HOURS: Mon-Sat, 8AM to 10PM
CLOSED SUNDAY

WHAT TO EXPECT: Casual Greek Cuisine • Good for families
Family owned & operated • Lots of parking

CARRYOUT/DELIVERY INFO: Order online or through the Toast
app. Full menu available for carryout and delivery. Delivery
available through Uber Eats and Bite Squad.

SCAN FOR MENU

SOME BASICS
Reservations:	NO
Spirits:	BEER/WINE
Parking:	LOT
Outdoor Dining:	NO

ATMOSPHERE

935 North Beneva Road
941-203-8542

SARASOTA COMMONS	PIZZA	COST: $$

HOURS: Wed & Thur, 4PM to 9PM • Fri & Sat, 4PM to 10PM
Sun, 5PM to 9PM • CLOSED TUESDAY

WHAT TO EXPECT: Fantastic Neapolitan pizza • Small, cozy setting
Italian cuisine • Lots of parking

CARRYOUT/DELIVERY INFO: Full menu available for carryout.
Delivery through Postmates, Uber Eats, and Door Dash.

SCAN FOR INFO

SOME BASICS
Reservations:	YES
Spirits:	BEER/WINE
Parking:	LOT
Outdoor Dining:	NO

BAKER AND WIFE

2157 Siesta Drive
941-960-1765
bakerwife.com

SOUTHGATE	AMERICAN	COST: $$

HOURS: Thur-Sat, 5PM to 9PM

WHAT TO EXPECT: Artisan pizza • Casual atmosphere
Lots of dessert choices • OpenTable Reservations

CARRYOUT/DELIVERY INFO: Online ordering available. Full menu
available for carryout. Delivery not available.

SCAN FOR MENU

SOME BASICS
Reservations:	YES
Spirits:	FULL BAR
Parking:	LOT
Outdoor Dining:	YES

BAVARO'S PIZZA NAPOLETANA & PASTERIA

27 Fletcher Avenue
941-552-9131
bavarospizza.com

DOWNTOWN	PIZZA	COST: $$

HOURS: Sun-Thur, 5PM to 9PM • Fri & Sat, 5PM to 10PM

WHAT TO EXPECT: Casual Italian • Good for families • Pizza!
Gluten free options • OpenTable reservations

CARRYOUT/DELIVERY INFO: Order online or through the Toast app. Full menu available for carryout and delivery. Delivery available through Uber Eats and Bite Squad.

SCAN FOR MENU

SOME BASICS

Reservations:	YES
Spirits:	FULL BAR
Parking:	LOT/STREET
Outdoor Dining:	YES

BEACH BISTRO

6600 Gulf Drive
941-778-6444
beachbistro.com

HOLMES BEACH	AMERICAN	COST: $$$$

HOURS: Daily, 5PM to 10PM

WHAT TO EXPECT: Fine dining • Beautiful gulf views • Romantic
Newly upgraded HVAC for a safe dining experience

CARRYOUT/DELIVERY INFO: Carryout and delivery not available.

SCAN FOR MENU

SOME BASICS

Reservations:	YES
Spirits:	FULL BAR
Parking:	VALET
Outdoor Dining:	YES

THE BEACH HOUSE RESTAURANT
200 Gulf Drive North
941-779-2222
beachhousedining.com

BRADENTON BEACH	AMERICAN	COST: $$$

HOURS: Daily, 11:30AM to 10PM

WHAT TO EXPECT: Great for a date • Florida seafood
Nice wine list • Lots of outdoor dining space

CARRYOUT/DELIVERY INFO: Order online or through Toast app.
Full menu is available for carryout. Delivery not available.

SCAN FOR MENU

SOME BASICS

Reservations:	NO
Spirits:	FULL BAR
Parking:	LOT
Outdoor Dining:	YES

BEVARDI'S SALUTE! RESTAURANT
23 North Lemon Avenue
941-365-1020
salutesarasota.com

DOWNTOWN	ITALIAN	COST: $$

HOURS: Tue-Thur, 4PM to 10PM • Fri & Sat, 4PM to 11PM
Sun, 4PM to 10PM • CLOSED MONDAY

WHAT TO EXPECT: Live music • In-house catering
OpenTable reservations • Nice outdoor dining

CARRYOUT/DELIVERY INFO: Online ordering. Full menu available
for carryout and delivery. Delivery available through Bite Squad.

SCAN FOR MENU

SOME BASICS

Reservations:	YES
Spirits:	FULL BAR
Parking:	STREET/LOT
Outdoor Dining:	YES

BIG WATER FISH MARKET

6641 Midnight Pass Road
941-554-8101
bigwaterfishmarket.com

SIESTA KEY	SEAFOOD	COST: $$

HOURS: Mon-Sat, 11AM to 9PM • Sunday, 12PM to 8PM

WHAT TO EXPECT: Fresh fish market • Casual dining
SK south bridge location • Key lime pie!

CARRYOUT/DELIVERY INFO: Online menu. Phone-in ordering only. Curbside pick up available. Delivery not available.

SCAN FOR MENU

SOME BASICS
Reservations:	NO
Spirits:	BEER/WINE
Parking:	LOT
Outdoor Dining:	NO

BIJOU CAFÉ

1287 First Street
941-366-8111
bijoucafe.net

DOWNTOWN	AMERICAN	COST: $$$

HOURS: Mon-Fri, 11:30AM to 2PM • Mon-Sat, 5PM to Close
CLOSED SUNDAY (summer only)

WHAT TO EXPECT: Great for a date • Excellent wine list
OpenTable reservations • Private dining program

CARRYOUT/DELIVERY INFO: Online ordering available. Full menu available for carryout. Curbside and contactless pick up. Delivery not available.

SCAN FOR MENU

SOME BASICS
Reservations:	YES
Spirits:	FULL BAR
Parking:	VALET
Outdoor Dining:	YES

BLU KOUZINA
25 North Boulevard of Presidents
941-388-2619
blukouzina.com/US

ST. ARMANDS	GREEK	COST: $$$

HOURS: Mon-Fri, 8:30AM to 3PM • Sat & Sun, 8AM to 3PM
Mon-Sun, 5PM to 9:30PM

WHAT TO EXPECT: Nice wine list • REAL Greek cuisine
OpenTable reservations • Many small plate appetizers

CARRYOUT/DELIVERY INFO: Full menu is available for carryout.
Curbside pick up available. Delivery not available.

SOME BASICS
Reservations:	YES
Spirits:	BEER/WINE
Parking:	STREET
Outdoor Dining:	YES

SCAN FOR MENU

THE BLUE ROOSTER
1525 4th Street
941-388-7539
blueroostersrq.com

ROSEMARY DIST.	AMERICAN	COST: $$

HOURS: Wed, 5PM to 10:30PM • Thur, 5PM to 11PM
Fri & Sat, 5PM to 11:30PM • Sun, 11AM to 2:30PM

WHAT TO EXPECT: Fun for a date night • Great fried chicken!
Excellent LIVE music • Happy hour

CARRYOUT/DELIVERY INFO: Online ordering available. Full menu
available for carryout. Curbside and contactless pick up.
Delivery not available.

SOME BASICS
Reservations:	NO
Spirits:	FULL BAR
Parking:	STREET
Outdoor Dining:	NO

SCAN FOR MENU

BOCA SARASOTA

19 South Lemon Avenue
941-256-3565
bocasarasota.com

DOWNTOWN	AMERICAN	COST: $$

HOURS: Mon-Fri, 11AM to 10PM • Sat, 10AM to 11PM
Sun, 10AM to 10PM

WHAT TO EXPECT: Sat & Sun Brunch • Online reservations
Classic cocktails • Craft beer selections

CARRYOUT/DELIVERY INFO: Online ordering. Full menu available
for carryout and delivery. Curbside pick up. Delivery available
through Uber Eats.

SCAN FOR MENU

SOME BASICS

Reservations:	YES
Spirits:	FULL BAR
Parking:	STREET
Outdoor Dining:	YES

THE BODHI TREE

1938 Adams Lane
941-702-8552
bodhitreecafesrq.com

TOWLES COURT	MEDITERRANEAN	COST: $$

HOURS: Thur-Sat, 5PM to 8:30PM

WHAT TO EXPECT: Casual atmosphere • Daily specials
Family owned and operated

CARRYOUT/DELIVERY INFO: Special menu available for carryout
and delivery. Curbside pick up. Free delivery in the downtown
Sarasota area.

SCAN FOR MENU

SOME BASICS

Reservations:	YES
Spirits:	BEER/WINE
Parking:	LOT/STREET
Outdoor Dining:	YES

BOHEMIOS WINE & BEER TAPAS BAR

`NEW`

3246 Clark Road
941-260-9784
srqbohemios.com

TAPAS	COST: $$

HOURS: Mon-Thur, 4PM to 10PM • Fri & Sat, 4PM to 12AM
CLOSED SUNDAY

WHAT TO EXPECT: Good sized wine list • Great small plate dishes
Intimate dining atmosphere • Lots of parking

CARRYOUT/DELIVERY INFO: Full menu available for carryout.
Delivery through Postmates, Uber Eats, and Grubhub.

SCAN FOR MENU

SOME BASICS
Reservations:	YES
Spirits:	BEER/WINE
Parking:	LOT
Outdoor Dining:	NO

BONJOUR FRENCH CAFÉ

5214 Ocean Boulevard
941-346-0600
bonjourfrenchcafe.com

SIESTA KEY	FRENCH	COST: $$

HOURS: Daily, 7AM to 2:30PM

WHAT TO EXPECT: Super casual • Great outdoor dining
Great crepes!

CARRYOUT/DELIVERY INFO: Full menu available for carryout.
Delivery not available.

SCAN FOR MENU

SOME BASICS
Reservations:	NONE
Spirits:	BEER/WINE
Parking:	STREET
Outdoor Dining:	YES

"Behind the Scenes" Look at the Sarasota Farmers Market

By Ciera Coleman, Market Manager

It's Saturday morning. While most folks are still cozy in their beds, with dreams of empanadas and fresh-baked loaves of sourdough in their heads, the staff and vendors at the Sarasota Farmers Market are working hard to put together one of the very best farmers markets in the country - right here in Sarasota.

At 4:00am, the Market Manager and her staff arrive. Twinkling lights sparkle in the palm trees on Lemon Avenue matching the stars still bright in the night sky. The Market footprint - running from Pineapple Avenue to First Street - is cleared of any vehicles or other safety concerns that may pose an issue for the coming crowds.

Also in the early morning hours, Kinsey's and SWFL Produce unload their large trucks and arrange beautiful displays of fresh fruits and vegetables across the Market. During the growing season, Worden Farm, an organic farm from Punta Gorda, arrives with an amazing assortment of fresh vegetables - and sunflowers as big as your head!

Keeping everyone smiling and laughing, owners of Herbeque, Herb and Danielle, arrive early as well. They get to work right away setting up their large, wood-fired smoker, so their fresh racks of ribs and smoked brisket will be ready by the time customers start coming around for a tasty breakfast or lunch.

As the morning progresses, other Vendors trickle in and begin setting up their tents. Local artisans, originally from all over the world, begin putting together displays of items that can't easily be found anywhere else - from beautiful works of art in all mediums to stunning hand-crafted jewelry, from sea sponges to soaps and candles, groovy tie-dye, and more. One thing that makes the Sarasota Farmers Market so special is that each week, the actual artisan is present at the Market - so customers get an opportunity to meet the maker of their favorite items.

The sun begins to rise, casting a peachy hue over all of downtown Sarasota. Yogis - of all skill levels and ages - can be spotted making their way to the Mermaid Fountain in Paul Thorpe Park for free sunrise yoga, a gentle 45-minute session led by nearby Pineapple Yoga Studio.

At 7:00am, the Market opens. Early Bird shoppers with grocery lists in hand arrive for the freshest seafood catch and the pick of their favorite produce. The robust smell of coffee fills the air - with vendors on both sides of the Market to satisfy any caffeine cravings (O & A Coffee & Supply on the North end of Lemon and Jimmy's Java on the South end - you won't be disappointed with either option!)

At 9:00am, the featured musician starts playing and the atmosphere of the Market shifts, with more customers filling the streets, some with unique (and leashed, well-behaved) pets in tow. (Dog-watching at the Market is a must!)

The Market is alive with activity. Customers are spotted strolling through with gorgeous plants - everything from unique and hard-to-find house plants to native shrubs and edibles, exotic orchids, bonsais, and bromeliads - and even rare fruit trees you can't find anywhere else. Logan at Suncoast Florist works hard assembling custom bouquets of fresh flowers, and Instagrammers can be spotted working to get their best photo of their finds in front of the gorgeous downtown Sarasota backdrop.

Many customers use the Market as an opportunity to stock their pantries - picking up staples like eggs and freshly butchered meat, and taking home special finds like jams, pickled fruits and veggies, and locally produced organic sauerkraut. And don't forget the snacks! Pick up some kettle corn from Kettle Cornball and dehydrated snacks from All Dried Up to keep even the pickiest snackers happy.

Lunchtime is always a happening time for the Market; the streets fill up with friends and family who are all excited to pick up their culinary favorites. There is lots of unique, amazing food to choose from - including cuisines from all over the world. You can try authentic Central Asian dishes from Cuni Tuni, plant-based Puerto Rican meals from Sol Foodz, traditional hummus bi tahini from Authentically Lebanese, and the best crepes this side of the Atlantic at Traditional French Crepes. End-capping the Market at the intersection of Lemon and Pineapple Avenues, local favorites Polpo Pizza Co. sell artisan, chef-created pizzas with unique and delectable toppings (try the bee sting - featuring their signature hot honey drizzle!)

At 1:00pm, vendors start packing up to go home. Just as quickly as the Market came together, the streets are cleared and vendors go home to get ready for next week.

Founded in 1979, The Sarasota Farmers Market, has been recognized as "one of the number one" farmers markets in the state of Florida. Visit the market in Downtown Sarasota, 7am to 1pm every Saturday, rain or shine. For more information visit sarasotafarmersmarket.org.

BREAKFAST AT VICTORIA'S NEW

4141 South Tamiami Trail
941-923-6441
breakfastatvictorias.com

SOUTH TRAIL	AMERICAN	COST: $$

HOURS: Tue-Sat, 7:30AM to 2:30PM • Sun, 9AM to 3PM
CLOSED MONDAY

WHAT TO EXPECT: Casual breakfast & lunch spot • Bakery! Good for small groups • Lots of parking

CARRYOUT/DELIVERY INFO: Full menu available for carryout. Delivery available through Uber Eats and Grubhub.

SCAN FOR MENU

SOME BASICS

Reservations:	NONE
Spirits:	BEER/WINE
Parking:	LOT
Outdoor Dining:	YES

THE BREAKFAST HOUSE
1817 Fruitville Road
941-366-6860

DOWNTOWN	AMERICAN	COST: $$

HOURS: Tue-Sun, 8AM to 2PM • CLOSED MONDAY

WHAT TO EXPECT: Charming atmosphere • Breakfast & lunch
Great omelets • Eclectic

CARRYOUT/DELIVERY INFO: Full menu available for carryout and delivery. Curbside pick up. Delivery available through Grubhub.

SCAN FOR INFO

SOME BASICS
Reservations:	NO
Spirits:	NONE
Parking:	LOT
Outdoor Dining:	YES

BRICK'S SMOKED MEATS
1528 State Street
941-993-1435
brickssmokedmeats.com

DOWNTOWN	BBQ	COST: $$

HOURS: Sun-Thur, 11AM to 10PM • Fri & Sat, 11AM to 11PM

WHAT TO EXPECT: State Street garage • BBQ, BBQ, BBQ
Good local beer list • Upbeat atmosphere • Catering

CARRYOUT/DELIVERY INFO: Online Ordering. Full menu available for carryout and delivery. Curbside pick up. Delivery available through Bite Squad, Uber Eats and DoorDash.

SCAN FOR MENU

SOME BASICS
Reservations:	YELP WAITLIST
Spirits:	FULL BAR
Parking:	STREET/GARAGE
Outdoor Dining:	YES

BRINE SEAFOOD & RAW BAR

2250 Gulf Gate Drive
941-404-5639
BrineSarasota.com

GULF GATE	SEAFOOD	COST: $$

HOURS: Lunch and dinner daily

WHAT TO EXPECT: Raw bar • Northeastern style seafood
Real Maryland style lump meat crab cakes

CARRYOUT/DELIVERY INFO: Full menu available for carryout.
Delivery not available.

SCAN FOR MENU

SOME BASICS
Reservations:	NO
Spirits:	FULL BAR
Parking:	LOT/STREET
Outdoor Dining:	NO

BUSHIDO IZAYAKI

3688 Webber Street
941-217-5635
bushidosushisrq.com

SUSHI	COST: $$

HOURS: Mon-Sat, 3PM to 9:30PM
CLOSED SUNDAY

WHAT TO EXPECT: Casual sushi • Good for families
Good sake selection

CARRYOUT/DELIVERY INFO: Full menu available for carryout.
Curbside and contactless pick up. Delivery not available.

SCAN FOR MENU

SOME BASICS
Reservations:	YES
Spirits:	BEER/WINE
Parking:	LOT
Outdoor Dining:	NO

BUTTERMILK HANDCRAFTED FOOD

5520 Palmer Boulevard
941-487-8949

SOUTH TRAIL	ITALIAN	COST: $$

HOURS: Tues-Fri, 7AM to 1PM • Sat, 8AM to 1PM
CLOSED SUNDAY & MONDAY

WHAT TO EXPECT: Great homemade baked goods • Small menu
Counter service only

CARRYOUT/DELIVERY INFO: Full menu available for carryout.
Delivery not available.

SCAN FOR INFO

SOME BASICS

Reservations:	NO
Spirits:	NONE
Parking:	LOT
Outdoor Dining:	YES

CAFÉ BACI

4001 South Tamiami Trail
941-921-4848
cafebacisarasota.com

SOUTH TRAIL	ITALIAN	COST: $$

HOURS: Tues-Sun, 4PM to 9:30PM
CLOSED MONDAY

WHAT TO EXPECT: Family owned since '91 • Private room available
Older dining crowd

CARRYOUT/DELIVERY INFO: Full menu available for carryout.
Curbside and contactless pick up. Delivery available through Bite
Squad.

SCAN FOR MENU

SOME BASICS

Reservations:	YES
Spirits:	FULL BAR
Parking:	LOT
Outdoor Dining:	NO

CAFÉ BARBOSSO

5501 Palmer Crossing Circle
941-922-7999
cafebarbosso.com

PALMER CROSSING	ITALIAN	COST: $$

HOURS: Tues-Sun, 4PM to 9PM • CLOSED MONDAY

WHAT TO EXPECT: Authentic NYC Italian • Casual dining
Fun dining experience • Good for groups

CARRYOUT/DELIVERY INFO: Full menu available for carryout
including family meals. Contactless, curbside pick up. Delivery
not available.

SCAN FOR MENU

SOME BASICS

Reservations:	YES
Spirits:	FULL BAR
Parking:	LOT
Outdoor Dining:	YES

CAFÉ EPICURE

1298 North Palm Avenue
941-366-5648
cafeepicure.com

DOWNTOWN	ITALIAN	COST: $$

HOURS: Daily, 11:45AM to 10:30PM

WHAT TO EXPECT: Great for a date • Wood fired pizza
Casual Italian fare • Palm Avenue garage

CARRYOUT/DELIVERY INFO: Full menu available for carryout and
delivery. No curbside service. Delivery through Bite Squad, Uber
Eats and Grubhub.

SCAN FOR MENU

SOME BASICS

Reservations:	YES
Spirits:	FULL BAR
Parking:	STREET/PALM GARAGE
Outdoor Dining:	YES

CAFÉ GABBIANO

5104 Ocean Boulevard
941-349-1423
cafegabbiano.com

SIESTA KEY	ITALIAN	COST: $$$

HOURS: Daily, 5PM to 10PM

WHAT TO EXPECT: Great wine list • Siesta Village location
Lots of parking • OpenTable reservations • Nightly specials

CARRYOUT/DELIVERY INFO: Online ordering available. Full menu available for carryout and delivery. Curbside and contactless pick up. Delivery through Bite Squad and DoorDash.

SCAN FOR MENU

SOME BASICS
Reservations: YES
Spirits: FULL BAR
Parking: LOT
Outdoor Dining: YES

CAFÉ IN THE PARK

2010 Adams Lane (Payne Park)
941-361-3032
cafeinthepark.org

DOWNTOWN	DELI	COST: $

HOURS: Sat-Thur, 11AM to 6PM • Fri, 11AM to 9:30PM

WHAT TO EXPECT: Super casual • Good for families & kids
Live music Fridays • Great outdoor dining

CARRYOUT/DELIVERY INFO: Most menu items available for carryout and delivery. Also, daily specials. Curbside pick up. Delivery through Bite Squad and Uber Eats.

SCAN FOR MENU

SOME BASICS
Reservations: NO
Spirits: NONE
Parking: LOT
Outdoor Dining: YES

CAFÉ L'EUROPE

431 St. Armands Circle
941-388-4415
cafeleurope.net

ST. ARMANDS	EUROPEAN	COST: $$$

HOURS: Tues & Thur, 4PM to 9PM • Fri & Sat, 12PM to 9:30PM
Sun, 12PM to 9PM • CLOSED MONDAY

WHAT TO EXPECT: Great wine list • Special wine dinners
Fine dining since 1973 • OpenTable reservations

CARRYOUT/DELIVERY INFO: Full menu available for carryout.
Curbside and contactless pick up. Delivery not available.

SCAN FOR MENU

SOME BASICS

Reservations:	YES
Spirits:	FULL BAR
Parking:	VALET/STREET
Outdoor Dining:	YES

CAFÉ LONGET

239 Miami Avenue W
941-244-2643
cafelonget.com

VENICE	FRENCH	COST: $$$

HOURS: Lunch: Mon-Fri, 12:00PM to 2:30PM
Dinner: Mon-Sat, 5:00PM to 9PM • CLOSED SUNDAY

WHAT TO EXPECT: Traditional French fare • Relaxed atmosphere
Homemade bread • OpenTable reservations

CARRYOUT/DELIVERY INFO: Most menu items available for
carryout. Delivery not available.

SCAN FOR MENU

SOME BASICS

Reservations:	YES
Spirits:	BEER/WINE
Parking:	STREET
Outdoor Dining:	YES

CAPTAIN BRIAN'S SEAFOOD RESTAURANT

8421 North Tamiami Trail
941-351-4492
captainbriansseafood.com

NORTH TRAIL	SEAFOOD	COST: $$

HOURS: Mon-Sat, 11AM to 8PM
CLOSED SUNDAY

WHAT TO EXPECT: Casual dining • Older dining crowd
Good for groups • Locally owned 30+ years

CARRYOUT/DELIVERY INFO: Most menu items available for carryout and delivery. Curbside pick up. Delivery through Uber Eats.

SCAN FOR MENU

SOME BASICS

Reservations:	YES
Spirits:	FULL BAR
Parking:	STREET/VALET
Outdoor Dining:	YES

CAPTAIN CURT'S CRAB & OYSTER BAR

1200 Old Stickney Point Road
941-349-3885
captaincurts.com

SIESTA KEY	SEAFOOD	COST: $$

HOURS: Daily, 11AM to 2AM

WHAT TO EXPECT: Good for kids • Super casual • Lots of seafood
Ohio State football HQ • Live music

CARRYOUT/DELIVERY INFO: Online Ordering available. Full menu available for carryout. Walk-up carryout station for pick up. Delivery not available.

SCAN FOR MENU

SOME BASICS

Reservations:	NO
Spirits:	FULL BAR
Parking:	LOT
Outdoor Dining:	YES

CARAGIULOS

69 South Palm Avenue
941-951-0866
caragiulos.com

DOWNTOWN	ITALIAN	COST: $$

HOURS: Daily, 4PM to 9PM

WHAT TO EXPECT: Casual dining • Palm Ave. gallery district
Good for kids • Good for groups

CARRYOUT/DELIVERY INFO: Online ordering available (special menu). Curbside pick up. Delivery available through Grubhub and DoorDash.

SCAN FOR MENU

SOME BASICS

Reservations:	YES
Spirits:	FULL BAR
Parking:	STREET/VALET
Outdoor Dining:	YES

CASEY KEY FISH HOUSE

801 Blackburn Point Road
941-966-1901
caseykeyfishhouse.com

OSPREY	SEAFOOD	COST: $$

HOURS: Daily, 11:30AM to 9PM

WHAT TO EXPECT: Vacation atmosphere • Local seafood
Boat docks • Old Florida feel • Live music

CARRYOUT/DELIVERY INFO: Full menu is available for carryout. Curbside pick up during non-peak hours. Delivery not available.

SCAN FOR MENU

SOME BASICS

Reservations:	NO
Spirits:	FULL BAR
Parking:	LOT
Outdoor Dining:	YES

CASK & ALE

1548 Main Street
941-702-8740
caskalekitchen.com

DOWNTOWN	AMERICAN	COST: $$

HOURS: Sun-Thur, 11AM to 12AM •Fri & Sat, 11AM to 2AM

WHAT TO EXPECT: Great craft beer selection • Casual adult spot
Try the Cask Classic Burger • Great for a downtown meetup

CARRYOUT/DELIVERY INFO: Full menu is available for carryout.
Delivery not available.

SOME BASICS

SCAN FOR MENU

Reservations:	NO
Spirits:	FULL BAR
Parking:	STREET
Outdoor Dining:	YES

CASSARIANO ITALIAN EATERY

313 W. Venice Avenue*
941-786-1000
cassariano.com

VENICE	ITALIAN	COST: $$$

HOURS: Lunch, Mon-Sat, 11AM to 3PM
Dinner, Mon-Sat 4:30 to Close • Sunday, 5PM to Close

WHAT TO EXPECT: Nice wine list • A UTC location, too
Great desserts • OpenTable reservations

CARRYOUT/DELIVERY INFO: Online ordering for delivery only.
Curbside pick up available for phone in carryout. Delivery through
Uber Eats and DoorDash.

SOME BASICS

SCAN FOR MENU

Reservations:	YES
Spirits:	FULL BAR
Parking:	LOT
Outdoor Dining:	YES

Florida Restaurant and Lodging Association Seal of Commitment

By Allison Chavez, FL Restaurant & Lodging Assn.

Across Florida, hospitality establishments are going above and beyond to heighten safety and sanitation standards by achieving the Florida Restaurant and Lodging Association (FRLA) Seal of Commitment. During the summer of 2020, FRLA launched the Seal of Commitment: the organization's highest designation for hospitality safety and sanitation. The Seal is a promise to guests that an establishment is committed to keeping their space clean and safe and that their staff is well trained in those procedures. Since the beginning of the COVID-19 pandemic, cleanliness has become a vital factor for guest comfort. When guests see a Seal of Commitment on an establishment's door, they can feel confident that it will be clean and safe.

When businesses began to reopen following the COVID-19 pandemic, many restaurants saw a need to improve guest confidence to return to dining rooms. During these unprecedented times, the FRLA Seal of Commitment was an opportunity for these establishments to provide more training to their staff, enhance their cleaning, and adjust their Standard Operating Procedures.

Seal of Commitment designees are required to go above and beyond what is required by the state for safety and sanitation training. To qualify for the Seal of Commitment, an establishment must complete a food manager, food safety, and FRLA COVID-19 Sanitation and Safety Course. Once all the courses are complete, and qualifications are met, an FRLA staff member visits the establishment to award the Seal.

The Suncoast area has led the way for Seal of Commitment designees. The first restaurant to achieve the Seal of

Commitment was Anna Maria Oyster Bar in Ellenton, FL. "We were proud to be the first of so many restaurants in Florida that have now received the FRLA Seal of Commitment," said John Horne, owner of Anna Maria Oyster Bar. "It's an honor to be part of the Suncoast's vibrant hotel and restaurant community that continues to maintain such high standards of excellence and care for our guests and staff." Since the launch, many other Sarasota-area establishments have also achieved the Seal of Commitment.

The Seal of Commitment program is available to all hospitality establishments in Florida – including FRLA members and non-members. For more information about the FRLA Seal of Commitment, including a full list of designees across the state, please visit frla.org/sealofcommitment. Look for this seal on restaurant listings in this guide.

C'EST LA VIE!
1553 Main Street
941-906-9575
cestlaviesarasota.com

DOWNTOWN	FRENCH	COST: $$

HOURS: Mon-Wed, 7:30AM to 6PM • Thur-Sat, 7:30AM to 10PM
Sunday Brunch, 8:30AM to 4:30PM

WHAT TO EXPECT: Outdoor tables • Relaxed cafe dining
Fantastic bakery • OpenTable reservations

CARRYOUT/DELIVERY INFO: Online ordering available for carryout (both locations). Delivery available through DoorDash.

SOME BASICS
Reservations:	YES
Spirits:	BEER/WINE
Parking:	STREET
Outdoor Dining:	YES

SCAN FOR MENU

CHA CHA COCONUTS TROPICAL BAR
417 St. Armands Circle
941-388-3300
chacha-coconuts.com

ST. ARMANDS	AMERICAN	COST: $$

HOURS: Sun-Thur, 11AM to 9PM • Fri & Sat, 11AM to 11PM

WHAT TO EXPECT: Good for kids • Lot of outdoor tables
Bustling atmosphere

CARRYOUT/DELIVERY INFO: Full menu available for carryout.
Curbside and contactless pick up, Delivery is not available.

SCAN FOR MENU

SOME BASICS
Reservations:	NO
Spirits:	FULL BAR
Parking:	STREET/GARAGE/VALET
Outdoor Dining:	YES

CIRCO
1435 2nd Street
941-253-0978
circosrq.com

DOWNTOWN	MEXICAN	COST: $$

HOURS: Mon-Thur, 11AM to 10PM • Fri, 12PM to 11PM
Sat, 11AM to 11PM • Sun, 11AM to 8PM

WHAT TO EXPECT: Super casual • "Taco & Bourbon Joint"
Good for a group • Catering available

CARRYOUT/DELIVERY INFO: Online ordering. Curbside and
contactless pick up available on request. Delivery is available
through Bite Squad, Uber Eats and DoorDash.

SCAN FOR MENU

SOME BASICS
Reservations:	NO
Spirits:	FULL BAR
Parking:	STREET/GARAGE
Outdoor Dining:	YES

CLASICO ITALIAN CHOPHOUSE
1341 Main Street
941-957-0700
clasicosrq.com

DOWNTOWN	ITALIAN	COST: $$

HOURS: Mon & Tue, 11AM to 11PM • Wed-Fri, 11AM to 12AM
Sat, 10AM to 12AM • Sun, 10AM to 11AM

WHAT TO EXPECT: Great for a date • Live music • Energetic scene
Sat. & Sun. brunch

CARRYOUT/DELIVERY INFO: Online ordering. Full menu available
for carryout and delivery. Curbside pick up. Delivery available
through Uber Eats, Grubhub and DoorDash.

SOME BASICS

SCAN FOR MENU

Reservations:	YES
Spirits:	FULL BAR
Parking:	STREET/PALM GARAGE
Outdoor Dining:	YES

CLAYTON'S SIESTA GRILLE
1256 Old Stickney Point Road
941-349-2800
claytonssiestagrille.com

SIESTA KEY	AMERICAN	COST: $$$

HOURS: Daily, 4PM to 10:30PM

WHAT TO EXPECT: Siesta Key casual • Good for groups
Convenient to SK south bridge

CARRYOUT/DELIVERY INFO: Online ordering. Full menu available
for carryout and delivery. Curbside pick up. Delivery available
through Uber Eats, Grubhub and DoorDash.

SOME BASICS

SCAN FOR MENU

Reservations:	YES
Spirits:	FULL BAR
Parking:	STREET/PALM GARAGE
Outdoor Dining:	YES

THE COLUMBIA RESTAURANT
411 St. Armands Circle
941-388-3987
columbiarestaurant.com

ST. ARMANDS	CUBAN/SPANISH	COST: $$

HOURS: Sun-Thur, 11AM to 9PM • Fri & Sat, 11AM to 10PM

WHAT TO EXPECT: Fantastic sangria • Excellent service
OpenTable reservations • Very busy in season

CARRYOUT/DELIVERY INFO: Full menu available for carryout.
Curbside and contactless pick up. Delivery not available.

SCAN FOR MENU

SOME BASICS
Reservations:	YES
Spirits:	FULL BAR
Parking:	STREET/GARAGE
Outdoor Dining:	YES

CONNOR'S STEAKHOUSE
3501 South Tamiami Trail
941-260-3232
connorsrestaurant.com

SOUTHGATE	STEAKHOUSE	COST: $$$

HOURS: Sun-Thur, 11AM to 10PM
Fri & Sat, 11AM to 11PM

WHAT TO EXPECT: Lots of parking • Large menu
Lots of wines by the glass • OpenTable Reservations

CARRYOUT/DELIVERY INFO: Full menu available for carryout
and delivery. Curbside and contactless pick up. Delivery available
through Grubhub and Uber Eats.

SCAN FOR MENU

SOME BASICS
Reservations:	YES
Spirits:	FULL BAR
Parking:	LOT/VALET
Outdoor Dining:	YES

THE COTTAGE
153 Avenida Messina
941-312-9300
cottagesiestakey.com

SIESTA KEY	AMERICAN	COST: $$

HOURS: Mon-Thur, 12PM to 10PM • Fri & Sun, 11AM to 11PM

WHAT TO EXPECT: Tapas • Siesta Village • Outdoor dining
Vacation atmosphere • Nice craft beer selection

CARRYOUT/DELIVERY INFO: Full menu is available for carryout.
Delivery not available.

SCAN FOR MENU

SOME BASICS
Reservations:	NO
Spirits:	FULL BAR
Parking:	STREET/VALET
Outdoor Dining:	YES

CRAB & FIN
420 St. Armands Circle
941-388-3964
crabfinrestaurant.com

ST. ARMANDS	SEAFOOD	COST: $$$

HOURS: Sun-Thur, 11:30AM to 10PM
Fri & Sat, 11:30AM to 10:30PM

WHAT TO EXPECT: Great for a date • Sunday brunch
Online reservations • Early dining options

CARRYOUT/DELIVERY INFO: Full menu available for carryout.
Curbside and contactless pick up. Delivery not available.

SCAN FOR MENU

SOME BASICS
Reservations:	YES
Spirits:	FULL BAR
Parking:	STREET/LOT
Outdoor Dining:	YES

THE CROW'S NEST
1968 Tarpon Center Drive
941-484-9551
crowsnest-venice.com

VENICE	SEAFOOD	COST: $$

HOURS: Lunch, Daily 11:30AM to 3PM
Sun-Thur, 4:30PM to 8PM • Fri & Sat, 5:30PM to 8:30PM

WHAT TO EXPECT: Water view • Good wine list
OpenTable Reservations

CARRYOUT/DELIVERY INFO: Full menu available for carryout.
Curbside and contactless pick up. Delivery available through
Uber Eats.

SCAN FOR MENU

SOME BASICS
Reservations:	YES
Spirits:	FULL BAR
Parking:	LOT
Outdoor Dining:	YES

CURRY STATION
3550 Clark Road
941-924-7222
currystation.net

DOWNTOWN	INDIAN	COST: $$

HOURS: Lunch Buffet: Mon-Sat, 11:30AM to 2:30PM
Dinner: Mon-Sat, 5PM to 9:30PM • CLOSED SUNDAY

WHAT TO EXPECT: Huge Indian menu • Lots of curries
A dozen naan and other breads • Online reservations

CARRYOUT/DELIVERY INFO: Full menu available for carryout.
Curbside pick up. Delivery available through Bite Squad, Uber
Eats, Grubhub and DoorDash.

SCAN FOR MENU

SOME BASICS
Reservations:	YES
Spirits:	BEER/WINE
Parking:	LOT
Outdoor Dining:	NO

DAIQUIRI DECK RAW BAR

5250 Ocean Boulevard*
941-349-8697
daiquirideck.com

SIESTA KEY	AMERICAN	COST: $$

HOURS: Sun-Thur, 11AM to 11PM • Fri & Sat, 11AM to 1AM

WHAT TO EXPECT: Great after beach stop • Super casual
Good for families • Dozens of frozen daiquiri flavors!

CARRYOUT/DELIVERY INFO: Online ordering available. Most
menu items available for carryout. Curbside and contactless pick
up. Delivery not available.

SCAN FOR MENU

SOME BASICS

Reservations:	NO
Spirits:	FULL BAR
Parking:	STREET
Outdoor Dining:	YES

DARUMA JAPANESE STEAK HOUSE

5459 Fruitville Road*
941-342-6600
darumarestaurant.com

FRUITVILLE RD	ASIAN	COST: $$

HOURS: Daily, 4PM to 10PM

WHAT TO EXPECT: Fun date night • Good for kids • Great for groups
Private parties

CARRYOUT/DELIVERY INFO: Full menu available for carryout and
delivery. Delivery through Bite Squad, DoorDash, Grubhub and
Uber Eats.

SCAN FOR MENU

SOME BASICS

Reservations:	YES
Spirits:	FULL BAR
Parking:	LOT
Outdoor Dining:	NO

DER DUTCHMAN

3713 Bahia Vista Street
941-955-8007
dhgroup.com

PINECRAFT	AMISH	COST: $$

HOURS: Mon-Thur, 6AM to 8PM • Fri & Sat, 6AM to 9PM
CLOSED SUNDAY

WHAT TO EXPECT: Good for kids • Easy on the wallet
Home cooking • Great pie • Groups welcome

CARRYOUT/DELIVERY INFO: Full menu available for carryout and
delivery. Curbside pick up for carryout. Delivery through Grubhub.

SCAN FOR MENU

SOME BASICS

Reservations:	NO
Spirits:	NONE
Parking:	LOT
Outdoor Dining:	NO

DIM SUM KING

`NEW`

8194 Tourist Center Drive
941-306-5848
dimsumsarasota.com

LAKEWOOD RANCH	ASIAN	COST: $$

HOURS: Lunch, Wed-Mon, 11AM to 2:30PM
Dinner, Wed-Mon, 5PM to 8:30PM • CLOSED TUESDAY

WHAT TO EXPECT: Dim Sum!! • Very casual atmosphere
Great for a quick lunch • Lots of parking available

CARRYOUT/DELIVERY INFO: Full menu available for carryout.
Delivery through Postmates, Uber Eats, Grubhub, and Door
Dash.

SCAN FOR MENU

SOME BASICS

Reservations:	NO
Spirits:	BEER/WINE
Parking:	LOT
Outdoor Dining:	NO

DIX CONEY CAFE

6525 Superior Avenue
941-927-1672
dixconeycafe.com

GULF GATE	AMERICAN	COST: $$

HOURS: Mon-Sat, 9AM to 5PM • Sun, 9AM to 3PM

WHAT TO EXPECT: Nice size portions • Diner style cuisine
Super casual atmosphere • Breakfast all day

CARRYOUT/DELIVERY INFO: Full menu available for carryout.
Delivery not available.

SCAN FOR INFO

SOME BASICS
Reservations:	NO
Spirits:	NONE
Parking:	LOT/STREET
Outdoor Dining:	NO

DOGGYSTYLE

1544 Main Street
941-260-5835
hotdogswithstyle.com

DOWNTOWN	AMERICAN	COST: $

HOURS: Mon-Sat, 10AM to 6PM
CLOSED SUNDAY

WHAT TO EXPECT: Hot dogs, lots of them! • Good for kids
Quick lunch spot • Fast, friendly service

CARRYOUT/DELIVERY INFO: Full menu available for carryout.
Delivery through Grubhub and Door Dash.

SCAN FOR MENU

SOME BASICS
Reservations:	NO
Spirits:	BEER
Parking:	STREET
Outdoor Dining:	YES

Roast Cauliflower Spinach Tomato Salad with Oven Roasted Tomato- Sherry Dressing

Chef/Owner Isaac Correa, Baker & Wife

CAULIFLOWER SALAD - INGREDIENTS

1 Cauliflower Head, rinsed and cut in quarters (leave the green outer stems intact)
1 pint cherry tomatoes, blistered, (blister using a handheld butane torch)
¼ cup parmesan cheese, grated
A cup or more of baby spinach
Kosher Salt
Coarse ground pepper
Extra Virgin Olive Oil to coat

DRESSING - INGREDIENTS

1 can (14 ounce) fire roasted tomatoes. We roast ours!
1 large garlic clove, coarsely chopped
1 medium shallot, coarsely chopped
3 tablespoons sherry vinegar
¼ cup extra-virgin olive oil
1 tbsp fresh Italian parsley, finely chopped
1 tbsp chives
Salt and pepper to taste

METHOD - FOR CAULIFLOWER

Preheat oven to 400 degrees. Place cauliflower in a large mixing bowl. Pour on enough olive oil to coat (a few tablespoons). Season generously with salt and pepper and toss gently until evenly coated. Toss with parmesan.

Lay cauliflower pieces out on a baking sheet. Drizzle any remaining oil from the bowl on top. Bake, turning once, until caramelized on edges about 15 minutes. Cool the Cauliflower in the baking sheet.

METHOD - FOR DRESSING
Place the fire roasted tomatoes, garlic cloves and sherry vinegar in a blender. On medium speed begin to blend the tomatoes until smooth. Open the blender top and blend in your olive oil making an emulsification. Season the dressing with salt and pepper, shallots, parsley, and chives. Let rest.

FINAL STEPS
In a mixing bowl toss the cauliflower, spinach leaves, (can add croutons) parmesan and some dressing. Arrange on a plate. Spoon some dressing around the plate and sprinkle some more parmesan add some blistered tomatoes - ENJOY!

At the restaurant we add toasted pine nuts and sourdough croutons to the salad. Give it a try.

Baker & Wife is located at 2157 Siesta Drive. For reservations call (941) 960-1765 or use OpenTable. www.bakerwife.com

---

DOLCE ITALIA
6551 Gateway Avenue
941-921-7007
dolceitaliarestaurant.com

GULF GATE	ITALIAN	COST: $$

HOURS: Mon-Thur, 5PM to 9PM • Fri & Sat, 5PM to 9:30PM
CLOSED SUNDAY

WHAT TO EXPECT: Great for a date • Good wine list
Lots of atmosphere • Family owned

CARRYOUT/DELIVERY INFO: Full menu available for carryout. Delivery not available.

SCAN FOR MENU

SOME BASICS

Reservations:	YES
Spirits:	BEER/WINE
Parking:	LOT
Outdoor Dining:	NO

DRIFT KITCHEN

700 Benjamin Franklin Drive (Lido Beach Resort)
941-388-2161
lidobeachresort.com/dining/drift

LIDO KEY	AMERICAN	COST: $$

HOURS: Daily, 7AM to 10PM

WHAT TO EXPECT: Upscale dining • Great gulf views
Lido Beach Resort

CARRYOUT/DELIVERY INFO: Full menu available for carryout.
Phone-in only. Delivery not available.

SCAN FOR MENU

SOME BASICS

Reservations:	YES
Spirits:	FULL BAR
Parking:	LOT
Outdoor Dining:	NO

DRUNKEN POET CAFÉ

1572 Main Street
941-955-8404
drunkenpoetcafesrq.com

DOWNTOWN	THAI	COST: $$

HOURS: Sun-Thur, 11AM to 10PM • Fri & Sat, 11AM to 12AM

WHAT TO EXPECT: Casual atmosphere • Good vegan options
OpenTable reservations • Great for small groups

CARRYOUT/DELIVERY INFO: Online ordering available. Full menu
available for carryout. Delivery through ChowNow, Bite Squad
and Postmates.

SCAN FOR MENU

SOME BASICS

Reservations:	YES
Spirits:	BEER/WINE
Parking:	STREET
Outdoor Dining:	YES

DRY DOCK WATERFRONT RESTAURANT

412 Gulf of Mexico Drive
941-383-0102
drydockwaterfrontgrill.com

LONGBOAT KEY	SEAFOOD	COST: $$

HOURS: Sun-Thur, 11AM to 9PM • Fri & Sat, 11AM to 10PM

WHAT TO EXPECT: Great water view • Local seafood • Happy Hour
Good for groups • OpenTable reservations

CARRYOUT/DELIVERY INFO: Full menu available for carryout.
Phone-in orders only. Delivery not available.

SCAN FOR MENU

SOME BASICS

Reservations:	YES
Spirits:	FULL BAR
Parking:	LOT
Outdoor Dining:	YES

DUTCH VALLEY RESTAURANT

6721 South Tamiami Trail
941-924-1770
dutchvalleyrestaurant.net

SOUTH TRAIL	AMERICAN	COST: $$

HOURS: Daily, 7AM to 9PM

WHAT TO EXPECT: Comfort food • Casual dining • Broasted Chicken!
Good for kids • Early dining crowd

CARRYOUT/DELIVERY INFO: Full menu is available for carryout.
Curbside and contactless pick up available.
Delivery not available.

SCAN FOR MENU

SOME BASICS

Reservations:	NO
Spirits:	BEER/WINE
Parking:	LOT
Outdoor Dining:	NO

DUVAL'S FRESH. LOCAL. SEAFOOD.

1435 Main Street
941-312-4001
duvalsfreshlocalseafood.com

DOWNTOWN	AMERICAN	COST: $$$

HOURS: Mon-Thur, 11AM to 10PM • Fri & Sat, 11AM to 11PM
Sun, 11AM to 10PM

WHAT TO EXPECT: Brunch • OpenTable reservations
Great Happy Hour • Free shuttle to the restaurant

CARRYOUT/DELIVERY INFO: Online ordering. Full menu available
for carryout and delivery. Curbside and contactless pick up.
Delivery through Bite Squad, Uber Eats and DoorDash.

SCAN FOR MENU

SOME BASICS

Reservations:	YES
Spirits:	FULL BAR
Parking:	STREET
Outdoor Dining:	YES

EL MELVIN COCINA MEXICANA

NEW

1355 Main Street
941-366-1618
elmelvin.com

DOWNTOWN	MEXICAN	COST: $$

HOURS: Sun-Thur, 11AM to 10PM
Fri & Sat, 11AM to 11PM

WHAT TO EXPECT: Casual Mexican cuisine • Good for groups
Great margaritas! • "Mex-Eclectic"

CARRYOUT/DELIVERY INFO: Full menu available for carryout.
Delivery through Grubhub and Door Dash.

SCAN FOR MENU

SOME BASICS

Reservations:	YES
Spirits:	FULL BAR
Parking:	STREET
Outdoor Dining:	YES

EL TORO BRAVO

3218 Clark Road
941-924-0006
eltorobravosarasota.com

MEXICAN	COST: $$

HOURS: Mon-Thur, 11AM to 8PM • Fri & Sat, 11AM to 9PM
CLOSED SUNDAY

WHAT TO EXPECT: Great for families • Super casual dining
Usually busy • Online reservations • Lots of parking

CARRYOUT/DELIVERY INFO: Full menu available for carryout.
Curbside and contactless pick up. Delivery available through Bite
Squad, Grubhub and DoorDash.

SCAN FOR MENU

SOME BASICS

Reservations:	YES
Spirits:	BEER/WINE
Parking:	LOT
Outdoor Dining:	NO

Get Your Sarasota Restaurant News!

FOLLOW, LIKE & SUBSCRIBE!
dineSarasota

ELEMENT: STEAK. SEAFOOD. PASTA.

1413 Main Street
941-724-8585
elementsrq.com

DOWNTOWN	AMERICAN	COST: $$$

HOURS: Tue-Thur, 4PM to 10PM • Fri & Sat, 4PM to 11PM
Sun, 4PM to 9PM • CLOSED MONDAY

WHAT TO EXPECT: Upscale downtown dining • Adult bar scene
Big city vibe

CARRYOUT/DELIVERY INFO: Full menu available for carryout.
Online carryout ordering. Delivery not available.

SCAN FOR MENU

SOME BASICS

Reservations:	YES
Spirits:	FULL BAR
Parking:	STREET
Outdoor Dining:	YES

EUPHEMIA HAYE

5540 Gulf of Mexico Drive
941-383-3633
euphemiahaye.com

LONGBOAT KEY	AMERICAN	COST: $$$$

HOURS: Wed-Sun, 6PM to 8:30PM • Curbside starts at 4:30PM
CLOSED MONDAY & TUESDAY

WHAT TO EXPECT: Great for a date • Online reservations
Fine dining experience • Great for special occasions

CARRYOUT/DELIVERY INFO: Most menu items available for
carryout. Curbside, contactless pick up available for carryout.
Delivery not available.

SCAN FOR MENU

SOME BASICS

Reservations:	YES
Spirits:	FULL BAR
Parking:	LOT
Outdoor Dining:	NO

EVOQ
100 Marina View Drive (Westin Sarasota)
941-260-8255
evoqsarasota.com

DOWTOWN	AMERICAN	COST: $$$

HOURS: Lunch & Dinner Daily

WHAT TO EXPECT: Handmade cocktail selections • Good wine list
Upscale comfort food • OpenTable reservations

CARRYOUT/DELIVERY INFO: Phone-in for carryout. Full menu
available for carryout. No curbside or contactless pick up.
Delivery not available.

SCAN FOR MENU

SOME BASICS
Reservations:	YES
Spirits:	FULL BAR
Parking:	VALET
Outdoor Dining:	NO

1592 WOOD FIRED KITCHEN & COCKTAILS
1592 Main Street
941-365-2234
1592srq.com

DOWNTOWN	GREEK	COST: $$

HOURS: Mon-Thur, 11AM to 9PM • Fri & Sat, 11AM to 10PM
CLOSED SUNDAY

WHAT TO EXPECT: Great casual dining • Online reservations
Nice street-side dining • Good downtown lunch spot

CARRYOUT/DELIVERY INFO: Full menu available for carryout.
Curbside and contactless pick up. Limited menu available for
delivery. Delivery through Bite Squad, Uber Eats and Grubhub.

SCAN FOR MENU

SOME BASICS
Reservations:	YES
Spirits:	BEER/WINE
Parking:	STREET
Outdoor Dining:	YES

How to Host a Wine Tasting Party

By Michael Klauber, Michael's on East

Looking to host a wine tasting party at home? I'm going to be sharing my best suggestions to ensure a successful and fun wine tasting experience!

1. Select the theme
Consider selecting a theme (country or wine region) to keep it focused. It's best to have 6-8 different wines for a tasting – 2-3 white wines and 3-4 red wines. In addition, we like to offer sparkling wine to greet guests as they arrive. For themes, you could select wines from countries like France, Italy or maybe South Africa. For regions, maybe Napa Valley, Tuscany or Oregon!

2. Structure
Organize the wines in rounds of two, side-by-side, for an appreciation of the contrast in styles and flavors. 2-3oz pours are a good amount to start with. It's fine to give each guest two glasses that they can reuse. They can dispose of leftover wine and rinse their glasses between each "flight". You can also serve the wines "blind" and have your guests guess what they are! Don't forget to make sure you have enough wine when they find a favorite and request more later!

3. Learn a little about wines
Take some time to research different wine regions and their wines and learn a little about them. This will make the selection process much easier when you have a general idea of what wines you want to choose, and it will also give you an idea of what food pairings to provide. Your local wine retailer can help you select wines to fit your theme.

4. Decide on food pairings

This one might require some research as well, depending on what wines you decide to go with. If you are having a themed event, this may help guide you in your food pairing decisions. At a minimum, assemble a trio of cheeses—something soft and creamy like brie; a crumbly, sharp variety like cheddar; and a bold option like a veiny blue. Maybe even include a mix of sweet and salty with grapes, dried fruits, charcuterie, and olives. Our rule is to select foods and sauces that will complement the wines - not overpower them - the wines are the star of the show!

5. Double check your supplies list

Supplies such as trays and serving boards and utensils can be used for a beautiful food presentation. You'll also want to make sure that you have enough wine glasses, plenty of water for your guests and a container for them to dispose of wines they do not finish. If possible, it's best to use large stemmed glassware. There are different styled stemware for red and white wines if you want to go that far.

6. Get festive with your décor

If you're hosting a themed event, this is a great opportunity to have extra decor that goes with the theme. Beware of using fragrant flowers or strong-smelling greenery - this can disrupt the nuances of the bouquet of the wines. There are so many fun things you can do to decorate for your wine tasting party!

7. Prepare ahead of time

To take the pressure off yourself, be sure to label everything from the snacks to the wines. You should provide some general information about the wines and have a printed list of the wines with room for guests to make notes. This way, everyone can focus on the experience and discuss it together in real time and have their notes to take with them.

Preparing for any type of party can get stressful, but I hope these tips have helped give you an idea of how to prepare for your wine tasting party!

Since 1987, Michael's on East has been leading the Sarasota fine dining scene. With 32 AAA Four-Diamond awards to their credit, you can always be assured of award-winning cuisine accompanied by outstanding service. Visit Michael's at 1212 South East Avenue, for reservations, 941-366-0007.

FIGARO BISTRO

1944 Hillview Street
941-960-2109
figaro-bistro.com

SOUTHSIDE VILLAGE	FRENCH	COST: $$$

HOURS: Tue-Thur, 5PM to 9PM
Fri & Sat, 5PM to 9:30PM CLOSED SUNDAY & MONDAY

WHAT TO EXPECT: Authentic, upscale French cuisine
Nice wine list • Try the Escargots de Bourgogne

CARRYOUT/DELIVERY INFO: Full menu available for carryout.
Delivery not available.

SCAN FOR MENU

SOME BASICS

Reservations:	YES
Spirits:	BEER/WINE
Parking:	STREET
Outdoor Dining:	YES

FINS AT SHARKEY'S

1600 Harbor Drive South
941-999-3467
finsatsharkys.com

VENICE	AMERICAN	COST: $$$

HOURS: Lunch, Daily, 12PM to 3PM
Dinner, Daily, 4PM to 10PM

WHAT TO EXPECT: Beachfront dining • Online reservations
Good wine list • "Steakhouse with a Serious Seafood Side"

CARRYOUT/DELIVERY INFO: Limited menu available for carryout.
Curbside pick up. Delivery not available.

SCAN FOR MENU

SOME BASICS

Reservations:	YES
Spirits:	FULL BAR
Parking:	LOT
Outdoor Dining:	YES

BURGER TIME!
SOME OF SARASOTA'S BEST

Hob Nob Drive-In • 1701 N. Washington Blvd. • 955-5001
WHAT TO EXPECT: Always one of Sarasota's best burger stops. Old school, nothing fancy. The "Hob Nob" burger basket is a must.

Indigenous • 239 S. Links Ave. • 706-4740
WHAT TO EXPECT: This one is always a pleasant surprise. Chef Phelps puts out a delicious burger. Can you say, bacon jam?

Island House Tap & Grill • 5110 Ocean Blvd. • 487-8116
WHAT TO EXPECT: They have a super secret prep method that turns out a perfectly cooked, juicy, and delicious burger every time!

Knick's Tavern & Grill • 1818 S. Osprey Ave. • 955-7761
WHAT TO EXPECT: Known for their burgers. Big and super tasty. For something a little different try a "Brunch Burger." Yep, egg topper.

Made • 1990 Main St. • 953-2900
WHAT TO EXPECT: Niman Ranch beef + billionaire bacon. What more do you really need to say? Delicious! Great sides, too.

Patrick's 1481 • 1481 Main St. • 955-1481
WHAT TO EXPECT: It's all about the burger at Patrick's. This restaurant is a downtown institution. Try it and you'll know why.

Shake Shack • 190 N. Cattlemen Rd. • 413-1351
WHAT TO EXPECT: If you have a Shake Shack in your town/city it has to make your "best of" list. Nothing quite like a ShackBurger.

Shakespeare's • 3550 S. Osprey Ave. • 364-5938
WHAT TO EXPECT: A caramelized onion & Brie burger! English pub atmosphere. Lots and lots of craft beer to wash it all down.

Tasty Home Cookin' • 3854 S. Tuttle Ave. • 921-4969
WHAT TO EXPECT: This one is just a bit different in the burger department. Think White Castle. 3 "Tasty Burgers" for $4.29!!

FLAVIO'S BRICK OVEN AND BAR

5239 Ocean Boulevard
941-349-0995
flaviosbrickovenandbar.com

SIESTA KEY	ITALIAN	COST: $$$

HOURS: Sun-Thur 4PM to 10PM • Fri & Sat, 4PM to 10:30PM

WHAT TO EXPECT: Homemade Italian cuisine • Brick oven pizza
Good meetup spot • Siesta Village location

CARRYOUT/DELIVERY INFO: Full menu available for carryout.
Curbside and contactless pick up. Delivery through DoorDash.

SCAN FOR MENU

SOME BASICS
Reservations:	YES
Spirits:	FULL BAR
Parking:	LOT
Outdoor Dining:	YES

GECKO'S GRILL & PUB

6606 South Tamiami Trail*
941-248-2020
geckosgrill.com

SOUTH TRAIL	AMERICAN	COST: $$

HOURS: Daily, 11AM to 10PM

WHAT TO EXPECT: Great to watch a game • Yelp waitlist
Good burgers • "American Pub Food"

CARRYOUT/DELIVERY INFO: Online ordering. Curbside and
contactless pick up. Delivery through Bite Squad.

SCAN FOR MENU

SOME BASICS
Reservations:	NO
Spirits:	FULL BAR
Parking:	LOT
Outdoor Dining:	YES

GENTILE BROTHERS CHEESESTEAKS

7523 South Tamiami Trail
941-926-0441
gentilesteaks.com

SOUTH TRAIL	AMERICAN	COST: $

HOURS: Mon-Sat, 11AM to 7PM • CLOSED SUNDAY

WHAT TO EXPECT: Philly experience • No frills dining
Easy on the wallet • Family owned • Good for kids

CARRYOUT/DELIVERY INFO: Full menu available for carryout.
Curbside pick up available. Delivery through Uber Eats, Bite
Squad and DoorDash.

SCAN FOR MENU

SOME BASICS
Reservations:	NO
Spirits:	NONE
Parking:	LOT
Outdoor Dining:	NO

GILLIGAN'S ISLAND BAR

5253 Ocean Boulevard
941-346-8122
gilligansislandbar.com

SIESTA KEY	AMERICAN	COST: $$

HOURS: Sun-Thur, 11AM to 11PM • Fri & Sat, 11AM to 12AM

WHAT TO EXPECT: Siesta Village • Live music • Younger crowd
Fun weekend hangout place

CARRYOUT/DELIVERY INFO: Full menu available for carryout.
Delivery not available.

SCAN FOR MENU

SOME BASICS
Reservations:	NO
Spirits:	FULL BAR
Parking:	STREET
Outdoor Dining:	YES

THE GRASSHOPPER

7253 South Tamiami Trail
941-923-3688
thegrasshoppertexmex.com

SOUTH TRAIL	MEXICAN	COST: $$

HOURS: Mon-Thur, 11AM to 9:30PM • Fri & Sat, 11AM to 10PM
CLOSED SUNDAY • Happy Hour, 3:30PM to 6:30PM

WHAT TO EXPECT: Easy on the wallet • Happy Hour
Good cocktail selection • Good for groups

CARRYOUT/DELIVERY INFO: Online ordering available. Curbside and contactless pick up. Delivery through ChowNow.

SCAN FOR MENU

SOME BASICS
Reservations:	YES
Spirits:	FULL BAR
Parking:	LOT
Outdoor Dining:	NO

GRILLSMITH

6240 South Tamiami Trail
941-259-8383
grillsmith.com

SOUTH TRAIL	AMERICAN	COST: $$

HOURS: Mon-Thur, 4PM to 9:30PM • Fri, 4PM to 10PM
Sat, 11AM to 10PM • Sun, 11AM to 9PM

WHAT TO EXPECT: Upscale casual • Plenty of parking
Good Happy Hour • Online reservations

CARRYOUT/DELIVERY INFO: Online ordering. Full menu available for carryout and delivery. Curbside pick up. Delivery through Uber Eats, Grubhub and Postmates.

SCAN FOR MENU

SOME BASICS
Reservations:	YES
Spirits:	FULL BAR
Parking:	LOT
Outdoor Dining:	NO

GROVE

10670 Boardwalk Loop
941-893-4321
grovelwr.com

LAKEWOOD RANCH	AMERICAN	COST: $$$

HOURS: Mon-Thur, 11:30AM to 10PM • Fri, 11:30AM to 10:30PM
Sat, 8AM to 10:30PM • 8AM to 10PM

WHAT TO EXPECT: Happy Hour • Culinary cocktails
Weekend brunch • OpenTable reservations

CARRYOUT/DELIVERY INFO: Online ordering. Full menu available
for carryout or delivery. Curbside pick up. Free delivery available.

SCAN FOR MENU

SOME BASICS

Reservations:	YES
Spirits:	FULL BAR
Parking:	LOT
Outdoor Dining:	YES

GULF GATE FOOD & BEER

6528 Superior Avenue*
941-952-3361
eatfooddrinkbeer.com

GULF GATE	AMERICAN	COST: $$

HOURS: Mon-Thur, 11AM to 1AM • Fri, 11AM to 2AM
Sat, 10AM to 2AM • Sun, 10AM to 1AM

WHAT TO EXPECT: Super casual • Good local beer selection
Later night menu • Sat. & Sun. brunch

CARRYOUT/DELIVERY INFO: Full menu is available for carryout.
No curbside pick up. Delivery through Bite Squad.

SCAN FOR MENU

SOME BASICS

Reservations:	NO
Spirits:	BEER/WINE
Parking:	STREET/LOT
Outdoor Dining:	NO

HARRY'S CONTINENTAL KITCHENS

525 St. Judes Drive
941-383-0777
harryskitchen.com

LONGBOAT KEY	AMERICAN	COST: $$$

HOURS: Restaurant - Daily, 9AM to 9PM
Deli - 11AM to 7PM

WHAT TO EXPECT: Great for a date • Longboat Key
Upscale Florida dining

CARRYOUT/DELIVERY INFO: Full menu available for carryout.
Curbside and contactless pick up. Delivery not available.

SCAN FOR MENU

SOME BASICS
Reservations:	YES
Spirits:	FULL BAR
Parking:	LOT
Outdoor Dining:	YES

HOB NOB DRIVE-IN RESTAURANT

1701 North Washington Boulevard (301 & 17th St.)
941-955-5001
hobnobdrivein.com

DOWNTOWN	AMERICAN	COST: $

HOURS: Mon-Sat, 7AM to 8PM • Sun, 8AM to 4PM

WHAT TO EXPECT: Easy on the wallet • Fun! • Great for kids
Sarasota's oldest drive-in. • Great burger!

CARRYOUT/DELIVERY INFO: Full menu available for carryout.
Curbside and contactless pick up available. Delivery not
available.

SCAN FOR MENU

SOME BASICS
Reservations:	NO
Spirits:	BEER/WINE
Parking:	LOT
Outdoor Dining:	YES

HOSHI SUSHI

6516 Superior Avenue
941-923-8888
hoshisushifl.com

GULF GATE	ASIAN	COST: $$

HOURS: Mon-Thur, 11AM to 10PM • Fri, 11AM to 10:30PM
Sat, 3PM to 10:30PM • Sun, 3PM to 10PM

WHAT TO EXPECT: Sushi • Hibachi and tempura dishes also
Great lunch specials • Casual sushi bar atmosphere

CARRYOUT/DELIVERY INFO: Full menu available for carryout.
Curbside pickup. Delivery through Postmates and Uber Eats.

SCAN FOR MENU

SOME BASICS
Reservations:	YES
Spirits:	BEER/WINE
Parking:	LOT/STREET
Outdoor Dining:	NO

THE HUB BAJA GRILL
5148 Ocean Boulevard
941-349-6800
thehubsiestakey.com

SIESTA KEY	AMERICAN	COST: $$

HOURS: Sun-Thur, 11AM to 10PM • Fri & Sat, 11AM to 11PM

WHAT TO EXPECT: Island dining experience • Good for families
Busy in season • Live music daily

CARRYOUT/DELIVERY INFO: Full menu available for carryout.
Phone-in orders only. Delivery not available.

SCAN FOR MENU

SOME BASICS
Reservations:	NO
Spirits:	FULL BAR
Parking:	STREET
Outdoor Dining:	YES

VEGETARIAN OR VEGAN?
HERE ARE SARASOTA'S BEST PLACES

Vegetarian and vegan lifestyles both offer a healthy way of eating. But, as any one who keeps either of these diets knows, dining out can sometimes be more than a challenge. I mean, how many grilled cheese sandwiches can one person consume? Don't despair. We're here to help. Sarasota has its share of options for those who choose a meat-free existence. Keep in mind that the places listed below may not be strictly vegan/veg only. But, they will offer some nice menu options.

Ka Papa Cuisine • 1830 S. Osprey Ave. • 600-8590
THE HIGHLIGHTS: Sarasota only 100% plant-based and vegan full service restaurant. Excellent menu of large and small plates.

Leaf & Lentil • 2801 N. Tamiami Trl. • 413-5685
THE HIGHLIGHTS: Lots of great variety. Vegan/veg, fast casual restaurant. Small plate and main plate options.

Lila • 1576 Main St. • 296-1042
THE HIGHLIGHTS: Named one of the best vegetarian restaurants in the country by OpenTable. Refined vegetarian cuisine.

Screaming Goat Taqueria • 6606 Superior Ave. • 210-3992
THE HIGHLIGHTS: Tacos, bowls, and more. Lots of vegan/veg options here. Your non-veg friends will be super happy, too!

Spice Station • 1438 Boulevard of the Arts • 343-2894
THE HIGHLIGHTS: Fantastic Thai cuisine. They've got a large section of vegetarian dishes on their menu. Cozy dining space.

Veg • 6538 Gateway Ave. • 312-6424
THE HIGHLIGHTS: The name says it best. Vegetarian + seafood. Dozens of their dishes can be made vegan too. Delicious!

IL PANIFICIO

1703 Main Street*
941-921-5570
panificiousa.com

DOWNTOWN	ITALIAN	COST: $$

HOURS: Daily, 10AM to 9PM

WHAT TO EXPECT: Great for lunch • Easy on the wallet • Quick
Good for kids

CARRYOUT/DELIVERY INFO: Online ordering. Full menu available for carryout and delivery. Delivery through Bite Squad, DoorDash and Slice.

SCAN FOR MENU

SOME BASICS

Reservations:	NO
Spirits:	BEER/WINE
Parking:	STREET
Outdoor Dining:	YES

INDIGENOUS RESTAURANT

239 South Links Avenue
941-706-4740
indigenoussarasota.com

TOWLES CT	AMERICAN	COST: $$$

HOURS: Tues-Sat, 5PM to 9PM • CLOSED SUNDAY & MONDAY

WHAT TO EXPECT: Great for a date • Fine dining, casual feel
Towles Court neighborhood • Limited outdoor seating

CARRYOUT/DELIVERY INFO: Carryout available. Special, rotating menu. Limited outdoor and indoor seating. Delivery not available.

SCAN FOR MENU

SOME BASICS

Reservations:	YES
Spirits:	BEER/WINE
Parking:	LOT/STREET
Outdoor Dining:	YES

INKAWASI PERUVIAN RESTAURANT

10667 Boardwalk Loop
941-360-1110
inkawasirestaurant.com

LAKEWOOD RANCH	PERUVIAN	COST: $$

HOURS: Mon, Wed-Thur & Sun, 12PM to 9PM
Tue, 5PM to 9PM • Sat, 12PM to 11PM

WHAT TO EXPECT: Casual dining atmosphere • Tapas Happy Hour
Lakewood Ranch Main Street location

CARRYOUT/DELIVERY INFO: Full menu available for carryout and delivery. Curbside and contactless pick up. Delivery through Bite Squad and Grubhub.

SCAN FOR MENU

SOME BASICS

Reservations:	YES
Spirits:	BEER/WINE
Parking:	LOT/STREET
Outdoor Dining:	NO

IRISH 31

3750 South Tamiami Trail
941-234-9265
irish31.com

SOUTH TRAIL	IRISH	COST: $$

HOURS: Mon, 3PM to 11PM • Tue-Thur, 12PM to 11PM
Fri & Sat, 12PM to 12AM • Sun, 12PM to 10PM

WHAT TO EXPECT: Lots of parking • Good for a game
Vibrant atmosphere • Daily specials • Happy Hour

CARRYOUT/DELIVERY INFO: Online ordering available. Full menu available for carryout. Limited menu is available for delivery. Delivery through Uber Eats.

SCAN FOR MENU

SOME BASICS

Reservations:	NO
Spirits:	FULL BAR
Parking:	LOT
Outdoor Dining:	YES

ISLAND HOUSE TAP & GRILL

5110 Ocean Boulevard
941-487-8116
islandhousetapandgrill.com

SIESTA KEY	AMERICAN	COST: $$

HOURS: Daily, 12PM to 10AM

WHAT TO EXPECT: Great craft beers • Fantastic burgers & tacos
Outdoor patio • Local favorite • Daily specials

CARRYOUT/DELIVERY INFO: Full menu is available for carryout
and delivery. Curbside pick up. Delivery through Bite Squad,
DoorDash, Uber Eats and Grubhub.

SCAN FOR MENU

SOME BASICS
Reservations:	NONE
Spirits:	BEER/WINE
Parking:	LOT
Outdoor Dining:	YES

ISLAND HOUSE TAQUERIA

NEW

2773 Bee Ridge Road
941-922-8226
islandhousetaqueria.com

	MEXICAN	COST: $$

HOURS: Daily, 11AM to 9PM

WHAT TO EXPECT: Great tacos! • Super casual atmosphere
Authentic al Pastor tacos • Good craft beer selection

CARRYOUT/DELIVERY INFO: Full menu available for carryout.
Delivery through Bite Squad.

SCAN FOR MENU

SOME BASICS
Reservations:	NO
Spirits:	BEER/WINE
Parking:	LOT
Outdoor Dining:	YES

JACK DUSTY

1111 Ritz-Carlton Drive
941-309-2266
ritzcarlton.com/en/hotels/florida/sarasota/dining/jack-dusty

DOWNTOWN	SEAFOOD	COST: $$$

HOURS: Breakfast, lunch, and dinner daily

WHAT TO EXPECT: Walking distance to downtown • Water view
Handmade cocktails • OpenTable reservations

CARRYOUT/DELIVERY INFO: Full menu available for carryout.
Delivery not available.

SCAN FOR MENU

SOME BASICS

Reservations:	YES
Spirits:	FULL BAR
Parking:	VALET
Outdoor Dining:	YES

JPAN RESTAURANT & SUSHI BAR

3800 South Tamiami Trail (Shops at Siesta Row)*
941-954-5726
jpanrestaurant.com

SHOPS AT SIESTA ROW	JAPANESE	COST: $$

HOURS: Lunch, Mon-Fri, 11:30AM to 2PM
Dinner nightly from 5PM to 9PM

WHAT TO EXPECT: Great for a date • Big sushi menu
Great lunch combos • OpenTable reservations

CARRYOUT/DELIVERY INFO: Online ordering. Curbside and
contactless pick up. Delivery through Bite Squad, Grubhub
and DoorDash.

SCAN FOR MENU

SOME BASICS

Reservations:	YES
Spirits:	BEER/WINE
Parking:	LOT
Outdoor Dining:	YES

JR'S OLD PACKINGHOUSE CAFE

987 South Packinghouse Drive
941-371-9358
packinghousecafe.com

AMERICAN	COST: $$

HOURS: Mon-Thur, 11AM to 9PM • Fri & Sat, 11AM to 10PM
Sun, 12PM to 6PM

WHAT TO EXPECT: Fun for a date • LIVE music
Great burgers & Cuban sandwiches

CARRYOUT/DELIVERY INFO: Full menu available for carryout and delivery. Curbside, contactless pick up. Delivery through Bite Squad.

SCAN FOR MENU

SOME BASICS

Reservations:	NO
Spirits:	FULL BAR
Parking:	LOT
Outdoor Dining:	YES

2022 SARASOTA FOOD EVENTS

FORKS & CORKS
WHEN: May 9 - 16th
WHAT: Sponsored by the Sarasota-Manatee Originals. Super popular food event! Wine dinners, seminars, AND the Grand Tasting. A must for Sarasota foodies. Tickets go very fast.
INFO: eatlikealocal.com/forksandcorks

FLORIDA WINEFEST & AUCTION
WHEN: TBD
WHAT: This charity event has been providing needed help to local children's programs for over 30 years. In the past couple of years, because of COVID, there has been on online auction.
INFO: floridawinefest.org

SAVOR SARASOTA RESTAURANT WEEK
WHEN: June 1-14th
WHAT: This restaurant week spans TWO full weeks. It features lots of popular restaurants and showcases three course menus.
INFO: savorsarasota.com

KA PAPA CUISINE

1830 South Osprey Avenue
941-600-8590
kapapacuisine.com

SOUTHSIDE VILLAGE	VEGAN	COST: $$$

HOURS: Wed-Sun, 5PM to 9PM

WHAT TO EXPECT: 100% plant based cuisine • Vegan
Casual "urban" feel • Southside Village location

CARRYOUT/DELIVERY INFO: Full menu available for carryout.
Delivery not available.

SCAN FOR MENU

SOME BASICS

Reservations:	YES
Spirits:	BEER/WINE
Parking:	LOT/STREET
Outdoor Dining:	YES

KARL EHMER'S ALPINE STEAKHOUSE

4520 South Tamiami Trail
941-922-3797
alpinesteak.com

SOUTH TRAIL	AMERICAN	COST: $$

HOURS: Mon to Sat, 9AM to 8PM
CLOSED SUNDAY

WHAT TO EXPECT: Great butcher shop • Home of the "TurDucKen"
German cuisine • Featured on the Food Network

CARRYOUT/DELIVERY INFO: Full menu available for carryout
and delivery. Curbside and contactless pick up. Delivery available
through DoorDash.

SCAN FOR MENU

SOME BASICS

Reservations:	NO
Spirits:	FULL BAR
Parking:	LOT
Outdoor Dining:	NO

KIYOSHI SUSHI
6550 Gateway Avenue
941-924-3781

GULF GATE	SUSHI	COST: $$

HOURS: Tues-Thur, 5:30PM to 9PM • Fri & Sat, 5:30PM to 9:30PM
CLOSED SUNDAY & MONDAY

WHAT TO EXPECT: Traditional sushi • Casual & comfortable
Beautiful presentations

CARRYOUT/DELIVERY INFO: *** At press time, we were not able to verify the carryout and delivery options for this restaurant. We suggest you call for their most up to date information. ***

SCAN FOR MENU

SOME BASICS
Reservations:	YES
Spirits:	BEER/WINE
Parking:	STREET/LOT
Outdoor Dining:	NO

KNICK'S TAVERN & GRILL
1818 South Osprey Avenue
941-955-7761
knickstavernandgrill.com

SOUTHSIDE VILLAGE	AMERICAN	COST: $$

HOURS: Mon-Fri, 11:30AM to 10PM • Sat, 5PM to 10PM
CLOSED SUNDAY

WHAT TO EXPECT: Casual dining • Busy in season • Family owned
Local favorite • Great burgers & daily specials

CARRYOUT/DELIVERY INFO: Full menu available for carryout and delivery. Curbside pick up. Delivery through Uber Eats.

SCAN FOR MENU

SOME BASICS
Reservations:	YES
Spirits:	BEER/WINE
Parking:	STREET/VALET
Outdoor Dining:	YES

KOJO

1289 Norht Palm Avenue
941-536-9717
eatkojo.com

DOWNTOWN	ASIAN	COST: $$$

HOURS: Sun, 11AM TO 11PM • Mon-Thur, 5PM to 11PM
Fri, 5PM to 12AM • Sat, 11AM to 12AM

WHAT TO EXPECT: Upscale Asian cuisine • Ramen, sushi & Bao buns
Next to Palm Ave garage • Online reservations

CARRYOUT/DELIVERY INFO: Full menu available for carryout.
Delivery not available.

SCAN FOR MENU

SOME BASICS

Reservations:	YES
Spirits:	FULL BAR
Parking:	GARAGE/STREET
Outdoor Dining:	YES

KOREAN SSAM BAR

1303 North Washington Boulevard
941-312-6264

	KOREAN	COST: $$

HOURS: Lunch, Tues-Sat, 11AM to 2PM
Dinner, Tues-Sat, 5PM to 9PM • CLOSED SUNDAY & MONDAY

WHAT TO EXPECT: Traditional Korean cuisine • Very casual
Family owned and operated

CARRYOUT/DELIVERY INFO: Full menu available for carryout and
delivery. Delivery through Door Dash, Uber Eats and Postmates.

SCAN FOR INFO

SOME BASICS

Reservations:	NO
Spirits:	BEER/WINE
Parking:	LOT
Outdoor Dining:	NO

L & L HAWAIIAN BARBECUE

NEW

5445 Fruitville Road
941-315-9008
hawaiianbarbecue.com/locations/sarasota

	HAWAIIAN	COST: $$

HOURS: Daily, 11:30AM to 8PM

WHAT TO EXPECT: Hawaiian BBQ! • "Plate" lunches
Yes, the have SPAM • Very casual • Good for a quick lunch

CARRYOUT/DELIVERY INFO: Full menu available for carryout and delivery, Delivery available through Bite Squad.

SCAN FOR MENU

SOME BASICS

Reservations:	NO
Spirits:	NONE
Parking:	LOT
Outdoor Dining:	NO

LA NORMA

NEW

5370 Gulf of Mexico Drive
941-383-6262
lanormarestaurant.com

LONGBOAT KEY	ITALIAN	COST: $$$

HOURS: Mon-Sat 5PM to 9PM
CLOSED SUNDAY

WHAT TO EXPECT: Authentic Italian Cuisine • Neapolitan pizza
Reservations suggested • Great dessert list

CARRYOUT/DELIVERY INFO: Full menu available for carryout and delivery. Delivery available using in-house service.

SCAN FOR MENU

SOME BASICS

Reservations:	YES
Spirits:	BEER/WINE
Parking:	LOT
Outdoor Dining:	NO

THE LAZY LOBSTER
7602 North Lockwood Ridge Road*
941-351-5515
sarasotalazylobster.com

NORTH SARASOTA	SEAFOOD	COST: $$

HOURS: Tues-Sun, 4PM to 9PM • CLOSED MONDAY

WHAT TO EXPECT: Great casual seafood • Early bird menu

CARRYOUT/DELIVERY INFO: Online ordering available. Most menu items available for carryout. Curbside and contactless pick up. Delivery not available.

SCAN FOR MENU

SOME BASICS

Reservations:	YES
Spirits:	FULL BAR
Parking:	LOT
Outdoor Dining:	YES

LIBBY'S NEIGHBORHOOD BRASSERIE
1917 South Osprey Avenue*
941-487-7300
libbysneighborhoodbrasserie.com

SOUTHSIDE VILLAGE	AMERICAN	COST: $$$

HOURS: Daily, 11AM to 9PM

WHAT TO EXPECT: Upscale dining experience • Good wine list
Busy bar scene • Reservations a must during season

CARRYOUT/DELIVERY INFO: Online ordering available. Full menu available for carryout and delivery. Curbside and contactless pick up. Delivery through Bite Squad, Uber Eats and DoorDash.

SCAN FOR MENU

SOME BASICS

Reservations:	YES
Spirits:	FULL BAR
Parking:	LOT/STREET
Outdoor Dining:	YES

LILA

1576 Main Street
941-296-1042
lilasrq.com

DOWNTOWN	AMERICAN	COST: $$

HOURS: Mon-Fri, 11AM to 9PM • Sat, 10:30AM to 9PM
CLOSED SUNDAY

WHAT TO EXPECT: Organic, locally sourced menu • Lighter fare
OpenTable reservations • Lots of veg/vegan options

CARRYOUT/DELIVERY INFO: Full menu available for carryout
and delivery. Curbside and contactless pick up. Delivery available
through Bite Squad.

SCAN FOR MENU

SOME BASICS
Reservations:	YES
Spirits:	BEER/WINE
Parking:	STREET
Outdoor Dining:	NO

THE LILY CAFE

NEW

4832 South Tamiami Trail
941-554-8700
tlcatthelandings.com

SOUTH TRAIL	AMERICAN	COST: $$

HOURS: Mon-Sat 8:30AM to 2:30PM
Sun, 8AM to 2:30PM

WHAT TO EXPECT: Breakfast & lunch spot • Great salads
Good for a group • Lots of parking

CARRYOUT/DELIVERY INFO: Full menu available for carryout.
Delivery not available.

SCAN FOR MENU

SOME BASICS
Reservations:	NO
Spirits:	BEER/WINE
Parking:	LOT
Outdoor Dining:	YES

LITTLE SAIGON BISTRO

2725 South Beneva Road
941-312-4730

VIETNAMESE	COST: $$

HOURS: Tue-Sat 10AM to 8PM
Sun, 10AM to 7PM • CLOSED MONDAY

WHAT TO EXPECT: Simple menu of Vietnamese dishes
Lots of parking • Great for a casual lunch or dinner

CARRYOUT/DELIVERY INFO: Full menu available for carryout.
Delivery not available.

SCAN FOR INFO

SOME BASICS

Reservations:	NO
Spirits:	BEER/WINE
Parking:	LOT
Outdoor Dining:	NO

LOBSTER POT

5157 Ocean Boulevard
941-349-2323
sarasotalobsterpot.com

SIESTA KEY	SEAFOOD	COST: $$

HOURS: Mon-Thur, 11:30AM to 9PM • Fri & Sat, 11:30AM to 9:30PM
CLOSED SUNDAY

WHAT TO EXPECT: Great for families • Lobster ++ • Siesta Village
Good for kids

CARRYOUT/DELIVERY INFO: Most menu items available for
carryout. Curbside pick up. Delivery not available.

SCAN FOR MENU

SOME BASICS

Reservations:	6 OR MORE
Spirits:	BEER/WINE
Parking:	VALET/STREET
Outdoor Dining:	YES

LOVELY SQUARE
6559 Gateway Avenue
941-724-2512
lovelysquareflorida.com

GULF GATE	AMERICAN	COST: $$

HOURS: Lunch - Daily, 8AM to 2PM
Dinner - Tue-Sat, 4PM to 8PM

WHAT TO EXPECT: Casual dining spot • Nice selection of crepes
Good for families

CARRYOUT/DELIVERY INFO: Full menu available for carryout.
Curbside pick up. Delivery not available.

SOME BASICS

SCAN FOR MENU

Reservations:	NO
Spirits:	BEER/WINE
Parking:	LOT
Outdoor Dining:	NO

MADE
1990 Main Street
941-953-2900
maderestaurant.com

DOWNTOWN	AMERICAN	COST: $$

HOURS: Tue-Fri, Lunch, 11:30AM to 2PM • Sun, 10AM to 2:30PM
Tue-Sat, Dinner, 5PM to 10PM • CLOSED MONDAY

WHAT TO EXPECT: Great for a date • Upscale, American cuisine
Chef driven menu

CARRYOUT/DELIVERY INFO: Online ordering available. Full menu
available for carryout. Curbside pick up. Delivery not available.

SOME BASICS

SCAN FOR MENU

Reservations:	YES
Spirits:	FULL BAR
Parking:	STREET/GARAGE
Outdoor Dining:	YES

SARASOTA MARKETS AND SPECIALTY STORES

A Taste of Europe • 2130 Gulf Gate Dr. • 921-9084
WHAT YOU CAN FIND THERE: Foods from twenty different European countries. Fresh deli, specialty cheeses, beer, wine, and more.

Artisan Cheese Company • 550 Central Ave. • 951-7860
WHAT YOU CAN FIND THERE: Cheese store. Hard to find small domestic dairies. Lunch menu. Classes. Knowledgeable staff.

Big Water Fish Market • 6641 Midnight Pass Rd. • 554-8101
WHAT YOU CAN FIND THERE: Fresh Florida fish. Great prepared seafood items. Just south of Siesta Key's south bridge.

The Butcher's Block • 3242 17th St. • 955-2822
WHAT YOU CAN FIND THERE: Meat market/butcher shop. Custom cuts, prime meats. Good wine selection. They have gift baskets.

Casa Italia • 2080 Constitution Blvd. • 924-1179
WHAT YOU CAN FIND THERE: A wide variety of hard to find ethnic items. Cheeses, deli, & more. Cooking classes. Prepared foods.

Geier's Sausage Kitchen • 7447 S. Tamiami Trl. • 923-3004
WHAT YOU CAN FIND THERE: Sausage & more sausage. Sarasota's best German market. Lots of smoked meats and deli items.

Karl Ehmer's Steakhouse • 4520 S. Tamiami Trl. • 922-3797
WHAT YOU CAN FIND THERE: Meat market. Skilled butchers, super helpful. Famous for Turducken. Also, full service restaurant.

M & M European Deli • 2805 Proctor Rd. • 922-1221
WHAT YOU CAN FIND THERE: European, Hungarian, & Polish grocery items. Great deli sandwiches. Borscht, goulash, & pierogis.

Morton's Gourmet Market • 1924 S. Osprey Ave. • 955-9856
WHAT YOU CAN FIND THERE: Upscale gourmet food items including a large selection of cheeses and wine. Great deli & carryout.

SARASOTA MARKETS AND SPECIALTY STORES

Morton's Siesta Market • 205 Canal Rd. • 349-1474
WHAT YOU CAN FIND THERE: Everyday grocery items plus a good selection of prepared foods for lunch and dinner. Cold beer.

Piccolo Italian Market • 6518 Gateway Ave. • 923-2202
WHAT YOU CAN FIND THERE: Italian market. Pastas, sauces, homebaked bread, and homemade Italian sausage. Sandwiches.

Southern Steer Butcher • 4084 Bee Ridge Rd. • 706-2625
WHAT YOU CAN FIND THERE: Big selection of pre-brined beef and chicken. Full butcher shop and lots of specialty items.

Walt's Fish Market • 4144 S. Tamiami Trl. • 921-4605
WHAT YOU CAN FIND THERE: Huge selection of fresh local fish & seafood. Stone crabs when in season. Smoked mullet spread!

MADEMOISELLE PARIS
8527 Cooper Creek Boulevard*
941-355-2323
mademoiselleparisutc.com

LWR	FRENCH	COST: $$

HOURS: Mon & Tue, 7:45AM to 5PM • Wed-Sat, 7:45AM to 9PM
Sunday Brunch, 7:45AM to 3PM

WHAT TO EXPECT: Traditional French fare • Casual European dining
Tartines, omlettes and more!

CARRYOUT/DELIVERY INFO: Online ordering. Full menu available for carryout and delivery. Curbside and contactless pick up. Delivery available through Bite Squad and Uber Eats.

SOME BASICS

SCAN FOR MENU

Reservations:	YES
Spirits:	BEER/WINE
Parking:	LOT
Outdoor Dining:	YES

MADFISH GRILL

4059 Cattleman Road
941-377-3474
madfishgrill.com

	SEAFOOD	COST: $$

HOURS: Mon-Sat, 11:30AM to 9PM • Sun, 11AM to 8PM
Sunday Brunch, 11AM to 2PM

WHAT TO EXPECT: Good for families • Daily specials
Happy Hour bites menu • Sunday brunch menu

CARRYOUT/DELIVERY INFO: Online ordering available. Full menu available for carryout and delivery. Curbside and contactless pick up. Delivery available through Bite Squad.

SCAN FOR MENU

SOME BASICS
Reservations:	YES
Spirits:	FULL BAR
Parking:	LOT
Outdoor Dining:	YES

MAIN BAR SANDWICH SHOP

1944 Main Street
941-955-8733
themainbar.com

DOWNTOWN	DELI	COST: $

HOURS: Mon-Sat, 10AM to 4PM • CLOSED SUNDAY

WHAT TO EXPECT: Great for quick lunch • Easy on the wallet
Lively atmosphere • Fantastic service

CARRYOUT/DELIVERY INFO: Most menu items available for carryout and delivery. Delivery available through Uber Eats and DoorDash.

SCAN FOR MENU

SOME BASICS
Reservations:	NO
Spirits:	BEER/WINE
Parking:	STREET
Outdoor Dining:	NO

MAISON BLANCHE

2605 Gulf of Mexico Drive (Four Winds Beach Resort)
941-383-8088
themaisonblanche.com

LONGBOAT KEY	FRENCH	COST: $$$$

HOURS: Tues-Sun, 5:30PM to 9:30PM • CLOSED MONDAY

WHAT TO EXPECT: Date night! • Special occasions
Excellent service • Great wine list • Online reservations

CARRYOUT/DELIVERY INFO: Special changing menu for carryout and delivery. Curbside and contactless pick up available. Limited delivery is available through the restaurant.

SCAN FOR MENU

SOME BASICS
Reservations:	YES
Spirits:	BEER/WINE
Parking:	LOT
Outdoor Dining:	NO

MANDEVILLE BEER GARDEN

428 North Lemon Avenue
941-954-8688
mbgsrq.com

ROSEMARY DISTRICT	AMERICAN	COST: $$

HOURS: Mon & Tue, 4PM to 11PM • Wed & Thur, 11AM to 10PM
Fri & Sat, 11AM to 11PM • Sun, 11AM to 10PM

WHAT TO EXPECT: Beer & lots of it • Elevated brewpub fare
North downtown location • Just a cool place to hang out

CARRYOUT/DELIVERY INFO: Online ordering available. Full menu available for carryout. Delivery not available.

SCAN FOR MENU

SOME BASICS
Reservations:	NO
Spirits:	BEER/WINE
Parking:	LOT
Outdoor Dining:	YES

MAR-VISTA RESTAURANT
760 Broadway Street
941-383-2391
marvistadining.com

LONGBOAT KEY	AMERICAN	COST: $$

HOURS: Sun-Thur, 11:30AM to 9PM • Fri & Sat, 11:30AM to 10PM

WHAT TO EXPECT: Great for families • Big list of specialty drinks
Water view • Old Florida feel

CARRYOUT/DELIVERY INFO: Online ordering available. Full menu available for carryout. Delivery not available.

SCAN FOR MENU

SOME BASICS

Reservations:	NO
Spirits:	FULL BAR
Parking:	LOT
Outdoor Dining:	YES

MARCELLO'S RISTORANTE
4155 South Tamiami Trail
941-921-6794
marcellosarasota.com

SOUTH TRAIL	ITALIAN	COST: $$$

HOURS: Mon-Sat, 5PM to 10PM
CLOSED SUNDAY

WHAT TO EXPECT: Nice wine list • Chef driven Italian cuisine
Intimate dining experience (10 tables)

CARRYOUT/DELIVERY INFO: Carryout and delivery not available.

SCAN FOR INFO

SOME BASICS

Reservations:	YES
Spirits:	BEER/WINE
Parking:	LOT
Outdoor Dining:	NO

MARINA JACK'S
2 Marina Plaza
941-365-4232
marinajacks.com

DOWNTOWN	SEAFOOD	COST: $$$

HOURS: Sun-Thur, 11AM to 9PM • Fri & Sat, 11AM to 10PM

WHAT TO EXPECT: Water view • Dinner cruises • Live music
Nice wine list • Live Music • Outdoor lounge

CARRYOUT/DELIVERY INFO: Carryout from patio only. Full patio menu available for carryout. Delivery not available.

SOME BASICS

SCAN FOR MENU

Reservations:	YES
Spirits:	FULL BAR
Parking:	VALET/LOT
Outdoor Dining:	YES

MATTISON'S CITY GRILLE
1 North Lemon Avenue
941-330-0440
mattisons.com

DOWNTOWN	AMERICAN	COST: $$

HOURS: Lunch - Daily, 11AM to 3PM
Dinner - Daily, 4:30PM to 10PM

WHAT TO EXPECT: Great for a date • Downtown meet-up spot
Live music • Great bar service • Happy Hour daily

CARRYOUT/DELIVERY INFO: Special limited menu available for carryout and delivery. Delivery available through Uber Eats, DoorDash and Bite Squad.

SOME BASICS

SCAN FOR MENU

Reservations:	YES
Spirits:	FULL BAR
Parking:	STREET
Outdoor Dining:	YES

MATTISON'S FORTY ONE

7275 South Tamiami Trail
941-921-3400
mattisons.com

SOUTH TRAIL	AMERICAN	COST: $$

HOURS: Mon-Thur, 11:30AM to 9PM • Fri, 11:30AM to 10PM
Sat, 4:30PM to 10PM • CLOSED SUNDAY

WHAT TO EXPECT: Large wine list • Brunch • Good value
Online reservations • Happy Hour menu

CARRYOUT/DELIVERY INFO: Full menu available for carryout.
Delivery available through DoorDash, Bite Squad, and Uber Eats.

SCAN FOR MENU

SOME BASICS

Reservations:	YES
Spirits:	FULL BAR
Parking:	LOT
Outdoor Dining:	NO

MEDITERRANEO

1970 Main Street
941-365-4122
mediterraneorest.com

DOWNTOWN	ITALIAN	COST: $$

HOURS: Lunch, Mon-Fri, 11:30AM to 2:30PM
Dinner, Daily from 5:30PM

WHAT TO EXPECT: Pizza • Good wine list • Italian specialties
Online reservations • Private party dining space

CARRYOUT/DELIVERY INFO: Online ordering available. Full menu
available for carryout and delivery. Curbside and contactless
pick up. Delivery through DoorDash.

SCAN FOR MENU

SOME BASICS

Reservations:	YES
Spirits:	FULL BAR
Parking:	STREET/GARAGE
Outdoor Dining:	YES

MELANGE

1568 Main Street
941-953-7111
melangesarasota.com

DOWNTOWN	AMERICAN	COST: $$$

HOURS: Lunch - Daily, 11:30AM to 2PM
Dinner - Daily, 5:30PM to 10PM

WHAT TO EXPECT: Great for a date • Adult dining experience
Open late night • Sophisticated menu options

CARRYOUT/DELIVERY INFO: Full menu is available for carryout
and delivery. Curbside and contactless pick up. Delivery available
through Bite Squad.

SCAN FOR MENU

SOME BASICS
Reservations:	YES
Spirits:	FULL BAR
Parking:	STREET
Outdoor Dining:	YES

MICHAEL JOHN'S RESTAURANT

1040 Carlton Arms Boulevard
941-747-8032
michaeljohnsrestaurant.com

BRADENTON	FRENCH-AMERICAN	COST: $$$$

HOURS: Mon-Thur, 5PM to 9PM
Fri & Sat, 5PM to 10PM • CLOSED SUNDAY

WHAT TO EXPECT: American "brasserie" • Upscale dining room
Great for a special occasion • Online reservations

CARRYOUT/DELIVERY INFO: Special carryout menu available.
Delivery not available.

SCAN FOR MENU

SOME BASICS
Reservations:	YES
Spirits:	FULL BAR
Parking:	LOT
Outdoor Dining:	NO

Mediterranean Shrimp

Chef Owner JR Garraus, JR's Old Packinghouse Cafe

INGREDIENTS

1lb. fresh shrimp (med-large), deveined and butterflied
3 red, yellow, or green peppers, sliced the same size as shrimp.
1 sweet onion, sliced in half
1 red onion, sliced in half
1 medium-large tomato, diced
1 TBSP fresh garlic, minced
1 TBSP tomato paste
1/3 cup white wine, clam stock, or fresh shrimp stock
1-2tsps olive oil
1 shallot, minced
½ cup Kalamata olives, pitted
3 green onions, chopped
4 oz feta cheese
Prepared Jasmine white rice, pasta, or mixed greens

METHOD - SHRIMP STOCK

Cover shells from shrimp in water and simmer for 45 minutes.
Discard shells.

METHOD - SAUTEED SHRIMP

Heat olive oil on medium high heat. Add peppers, onions, garlic,
shallots, and shrimp and simmer until sauce forms. Add tomato,
tomato paste, wine, fresh shrimp stock, broth or clam stock.
Cook until sauce simmers, about 2-3 minutes.

Garnish with olives, green onions, and feta. Serve over rice or
pasta or mixed greens.

*Visit JR's Old Packinghouse Cafe at 987 S. Packinghouse Rd.
(941) 371-9358. For more info visit packinghousecafe.com.*

MICHAEL'S ON EAST
1212 East Avenue South
941-366-0007
bestfood.com

| MIDTOWN PLAZA | AMERICAN | COST: $$$ |

HOURS: Tue-Thur, 5PM to 8:30PM • Fri & Sat, 5PM to 9PM
CLOSED SUNDAY AND MONDAY

WHAT TO EXPECT: Piano lounge • Catering • Fine dining
OpenTable reservations • AAA Four Diamond Award

CARRYOUT/DELIVERY INFO: Online ordering available.
Curbside and contactless pick up. Delivery available through the
restaurant.

SOME BASICS

SCAN FOR MENU

Reservations:	YES
Spirits:	FULL BAR
Parking:	VALET
Outdoor Dining:	YES

MICHELLE'S BROWN BAG CAFÉ
1819 Main Street (City Center Building)
941-365-5858
michellesbrownbagcafe.com

| DOWNTOWN | DELI | COST: $ |

HOURS: Mon-Fri, 7:30AM to 3PM
CLOSED SATURDAY & SUNDAY

WHAT TO EXPECT: Quick lunch • Easy on the wallet
Great meet-up spot • Super casual

CARRYOUT/DELIVERY INFO: Online ordering available. Full menu
available for carryout and delivery. Delivery is available through
the restaurant or Bite Squad.

SOME BASICS

SCAN FOR MENU

Reservations:	NO
Spirits:	BEER/WINE
Parking:	GARAGE/STREET
Outdoor Dining:	NO

MIGUEL'S
6631 Midnight Pass Road
941-349-4024
miguelsrestaurant.net

SIESTA KEY	FRENCH	COST: $$$

HOURS: Dinner, Daily from 5PM
Early Dinner Menu, 5PM to 6:30PM

WHAT TO EXPECT: Good wine list • Quiet atmosphere
Good early dining menu

CARRYOUT/DELIVERY INFO: Online ordering available. Full menu available for carryout. Delivery not available.

SCAN FOR MENU

SOME BASICS
Reservations:	YES
Spirits:	FULL BAR
Parking:	LOT
Outdoor Dining:	NO

MILLIES RESTAURANT
3900 Clark Road
941-923-4054
eatatmillies.com

	AMERICAN	COST: $$

HOURS: Daily, 7AM to 2:30PM

WHAT TO EXPECT: Casual atmosphere • Good for families
Lots of parking

CARRYOUT/DELIVERY INFO: Online ordering available. Full menu available for carryout. You must call ahead for curbside pick up. Delivery not available.

SCAN FOR INFO

SOME BASICS
Reservations:	NO
Spirits:	NONE
Parking:	LOT
Outdoor Dining:	NO

MONK'S STEAMER BAR

6690 Superior Avenue
941-927-3388
monkssteamerbar.com

GULF GATE	SEAFOOD	COST: $$

HOURS: Mon-Thur, 3PM to 12AM • Fri & Sat, 12PM to 1AM
Sunday, 12PM to 12AM

WHAT TO EXPECT: Steamed everything! • Dive bar/great food
Locals favorite • Late night menu

CARRYOUT/DELIVERY INFO: Most menu items available for
carryout. Delivery not available.

SCAN FOR MENU

SOME BASICS

Reservations:	NO
Spirits:	FULL BAR
Parking:	STREET/LOT
Outdoor Dining:	NO

MUNCHIES 420 CAFÉ

6639 Superior Avenue
941-929-9893
munchies420cafe.com

GULF GATE	AMERICAN	COST: $$

HOURS: Sun-Thur, 12PM to 3AM • Fri & Sat, 12PM to 4:20AM
Happy Hour, Daily, 12PM to 7PM

WHAT TO EXPECT: Crazy sandwiches! • Super laid back • Late night
Local favorite

CARRYOUT/DELIVERY INFO: Online ordering available. Full menu
available for carryout and delivery. Delivery available through Bite
Squad.

SCAN FOR MENU

SOME BASICS

Reservations:	NO
Spirits:	FULL BAR
Parking:	LOT
Outdoor Dining:	YES

99 BOTTLES TAPROOM

1445 Second Street
941-487-7874
99bottles.net

DOWNTOWN	BEER	COST: $$

HOURS: Mon-Thur, 3PM to 11PM
Fri - Sun, 9AM to 12AM

WHAT TO EXPECT: Big city feel • Knowledgeable bar staff
Small menu of good food • Great for an after work beer

CARRYOUT/DELIVERY INFO: Online ordering available. Full menu available for carryout. Curbside and contactless pick up. Delivery not available.

SCAN FOR MENU

SOME BASICS

Reservations:	NO
Spirits:	BEER/WINE
Parking:	STREET/GARAGE
Outdoor Dining:	YES

NANCY'S BAR-B-QUE

14475 State Road 70 E
941-999-2390
nancysbarbq.com

LWR	BBQ	COST: $

HOURS: Sun-Thur, 11AM to 8PM • Fri & Sat, 11AM to 9PM

WHAT TO EXPECT: Casual dining • Good for families
Catering available • Combo meals • Great pulled pork!

CARRYOUT/DELIVERY INFO: Online ordering available. Full menu available for carryout and delivery. Curbside and contactless pick up. Delivery available through Bite Squad and Grubhub.

SCAN FOR MENU

SOME BASICS

Reservations:	NO
Spirits:	FULLBAR
Parking:	LOT
Outdoor Dining:	YES

NAPULÈ RISTORANTE ITALIANO

7129 South Tamiami Trail
941-556-9639
napulesarasota.com

SOUTH TRAIL	ITALIAN	COST: $$$

HOURS: Mon-Thur, 11:30AM to 9:30PM
Fri & Sat, 11:30AM to 10:30PM • CLOSED SUNDAY

WHAT TO EXPECT: Upscale Italian dining • Great wood oven pizza
Very busy in season • Vibrant atmosphere

CARRYOUT/DELIVERY INFO: Full menu available for carryout
and delivery. Curbside and contactless pick up. Delivery available
through Bite Squad and DoorDash.

SCAN FOR MENU

SOME BASICS

Reservations:	YES
Spirits:	FULL BAR
Parking:	LOT
Outdoor Dining:	YES

NELLIE'S DELI

15 South Beneva Road
941-924-2705
nelliescatering.com

	DELI	COST: $$

HOURS: Mon-Fri, 7AM to 2:30PM • Sat, 8AM to 2:30PM
CLOSED SUNDAY

WHAT TO EXPECT: Deli & market • Great catering options
Casual dining • Good for families • Box lunches!

CARRYOUT/DELIVERY INFO: Full menu available for carryout and
delivery. Contactless pick up. Delivery available through
the restaurant.

SCAN FOR MENU

SOME BASICS

Reservations:	NO
Spirits:	NONE
Parking:	LOT
Outdoor Dining:	NO

SARASOTA
UPSCALE CHAIN DINING

Sarasota has a ton of great independently owned and operated restaurants. And, that's mostly what this dining book is all about. But, as with any decent size city, we've got our share of quality, upscale chain dining options, too.

We've taken the time to put together a list of some of our favorites. Just like the main section of the book, we didn't have the space to list them all. So, we curated a collection of the ones we think will give you a consistent and favorable dining experience.

We've tried to include a little bit of everything here for you. Some steakhouses, sushi, deli, and even pizza. You'll recognize most of the names I'm sure. There's something here for everyone.

Bonefish Grill • 3971 S. Tamiami Trl. • 924-9090
WHAT TO EXPECT: Upscale casual place to meetup with friends and enjoy drinks or dinner. Lots of seafood options. ($$)

Brio Tuscan Grille • 190 University Town Center Dr. • 702-9102
WHAT TO EXPECT: Italian cuisine. UTC. Online reservations. Lively atmosphere. Good for groups. ($$$)

Cooper's Hawk • 3130 Fruitville Commons Blvd. • 263-8100
WHAT TO EXPECT: Steaks, seafood, much more. Fantastic wine selection. Modern, casual dining. ($$$)

Capital Grille • 180 University Town Center Dr. • 256-3647
WHAT TO EXPECT: Big city steakhouse. Very upscale dining experience. Reservations/OpenTable. Private dining. ($$$$)

Chart House • 201 Gulf of Mexico Dr. • 383-5593
WHAT TO EXPECT: Fresh seafood. Nice gulf view. Always outstanding service. Classic upscale dining experience. ($$$)

Cheesecake Factory • 130 University Town Center Dr. • 256-3760
WHAT TO EXPECT: 200+ menu choices. Super large portions.
Happy Hour. Catering. Very busy dining atmosphere. ($$$)

Fleming's Prime Steakhouse • 2001 Siesta Dr. • 358-9463
WHAT TO EXPECT: Super high quality steaks + service. Private
dining. "Fleming's 100" wines. Happy Hour. ($$$$)

Hyde Park Steakhouse • 35 S. Lemon Ave. • 366-7788
WHAT TO EXPECT: Busy downtown location. Valet parking. Popular
Happy Hour. "Early Nights" menu. Private dining. ($$$$)

Kona Grill • 150 University Town Center Dr. • 256-8050
WHAT TO EXPECT: Heavy Asian influence cuisine. Sushi. Lively
dining experience. UTC Mall. Online reservations. ($$)

P.F. Changs Bistro • 766 S. Osprey Ave. • 296-6002
WHAT TO EXPECT: "Farm to Wok" Asian cuisine. Large menu. Busy,
vibrant atmosphere. Good for groups. Online reservations. ($$$)

Rodizo Brazilian Steakhouse • 5911 Fruitville Rd. • 260-8445
WHAT TO EXPECT: Brazilian steakhouse experience. Rotisserie
grilled meats. Table side service. Large gourmet salad bar. ($$$)

Ruth's Chris Steakhouse • 6700 S. Tamiami Trl. • 942-8982
WHAT TO EXPECT: Exceptional service. Older dining crowd. Large
selection of USDA prime steaks. Great wine list. ($$$$)

Seasons 52 • 170 University Town Center Dr. • 702-5652
WHAT TO EXPECT: Seasonal menu selections. 52 wines by the
glass. UTC Mall. Group dining options. Great service. ($$$)

Sophie's • 120 University Town Center Dr. • 444-3077
WHAT TO EXPECT: UTC inside Sak's 5th Avenue. "Ladies" lunch
spot. Intimate dining experience. Great for private parties. ($$$)

NEW PASS GRILL & BAIT SHOP

1505 Ken Thompson Parkway
941-388-3050
newpassgrill.com

CITY ISLAND	AMERICAN	COST: $

HOURS: Daily, 8AM to 5PM

WHAT TO EXPECT: Casual dining • Water view • More than burgers
Bait & tackle shop

CARRYOUT/DELIVERY INFO: Full menu available for carryout.
Delivery not available.

SCAN FOR MENU

SOME BASICS

Reservations:	NO
Spirits:	BEER/WINE
Parking:	LOT
Outdoor Dining:	YES

NICKY'S BISTRO

NEW

49 South Palm Avenue
941-330-1727
nickysonpalm.com

DOWNTOWN	AMERICAN	COST: $$$

HOURS: Wed-Sat 5PM to 10PM

WHAT TO EXPECT: Classic "Hollywood" style • Piano bar
Downtown Miromar Building location

CARRYOUT/DELIVERY INFO: Full menu available for carryout.
Delivery not available.

SCAN FOR MENU

SOME BASICS

Reservations:	YES
Spirits:	FULL BAR
Parking:	STREET
Outdoor Dining:	NO

OAK & STONE

5405 University Parkway*
941-225-4590
oakandstone.com

UPARK	AMERICAN	COST: $$

HOURS: Sun-Thur, 11AM to 10PM • Fri & Sat, 11AM to 12AM

WHAT TO EXPECT: Great for sports viewing • Lively atmosphere
Live music • Large beer selection • Pizza too!

CARRYOUT/DELIVERY INFO: Online ordering. Full menu available
for carryout & delivery. Curbside & contactless pick up. Delivery
through Bite Squad, Grubhub, DoorDash and Uber Eats.

SCAN FOR MENU

SOME BASICS

Reservations:	NO
Spirits:	FULL BAR
Parking:	LOT
Outdoor Dining:	YES

OASIS CAFÉ & BAKERY

3542 South Osprey Avenue
941-957-1214
theoasiscafe.net

AMERICAN	COST: $$

HOURS: Mon-Fri, 7AM to 1:30PM • Sat & Sun, 8AM to 1:30PM

WHAT TO EXPECT: Breakfast & Lunch • Casual dining
Very busy in season • Great bakery

CARRYOUT/DELIVERY INFO: Full menu available for carryout.
Curbside and contactless pick up. Delivery not available.

SCAN FOR MENU

SOME BASICS

Reservations:	NO
Spirits:	BEER/WINE
Parking:	LOT
Outdoor Dining:	YES

Make it at
HOME

Blackened Calamari
Sautéed with Lemon Lime Beurre Blanc

Knickole Barger, Knick's Tavern & Grill

INGREDIENTS

1 lb calamari, cleaned, bodies cut into 3/4-inch-thick rings,
tentacles left whole
2 tbsp extra-virgin olive oil
4 tbsp unsalted butter (1/2 stick)
2 tsp finely chopped garlic, 2 teaspoons shallots, finely chopped
1 tbsp coarsely chopped Italian parsley leaves
¼ cup dry white wine
¼ cup heavy cream
Salt to taste
Freshly ground black pepper
Juice of ½ small lemon & ½ small lime, the remainder cut into
wedges, for garnishing

METHOD: LEMON LIME BEURRE BLANC SAUCE

In saucepan, add 1 tablespoon of olive oil on medium heat. Add
shallots and garlic. Sauté 2 minutes. Add lemon and lime juice,
wine, and cream. Let reduce by half. Turn heat to low.

Divide butter into squares. Whisk into sauce a couple cubes at a
time until all butter is melted through. Reserve sauce in cool room
temperature area. (This can be plated now if you like).

METHOD: BLACKENED CALAMARI

Pat calamari dry with a paper towel.

Heat oil in a large frying pan over high heat until smoking.
Carefully add calamari in a single layer. Stir to coat with oil.
Lightly season with your favorite dry blackening seasoning. Cook,

tossing frequently, until squid is opaque and cooked through, about 1 to 2 minutes (do not overcook).

Serve on large platter, over the Beurre Blanc sauce. Place warm toasted garlic butter bread around plate. Add fresh parsley and citrus wedges for garnish and color. Enjoy!

Serves 3-4 as an appetizer

Knick's Tavern & Grill has been known as the area's "Cheers" since it opened its doors in 2002. It's a place that locals favorite and visitors return to. They've been serving a menu of delicious "contemporary comfort food" at their Southside Village restaurant for twenty years! Knick's is located at 1818 S Osprey Avenue. For reservations call, (941) 955-7761 or visit them at knickstavernandgrill.com.

THE OLD SALTY DOG
5023 Ocean Boulevard*
941-349-0158
theoldsaltydog.com

SIESTA KEY	AMERICAN	COST: $$

HOURS: Sun-Thur, 11AM to 9:30PM • Fri & Sat, 11AM to 10PM

WHAT TO EXPECT: Locals love it • Vacation feel • Cold beer
Busy during season • Siesta Village • Friendly bar staff

CARRYOUT/DELIVERY INFO: Online ordering available. Full menu available for carryout. Delivery not available.

SOME BASICS

Reservations:	NO
Spirits:	FULL BAR
Parking:	STREET
Outdoor Dining:	YES

SCAN FOR MENU

Sarasota Must Do Food Experiences

By Nita Ettinger
Must Do Visitor Guides

I love to cook, but I also love to eat out. I think we can all agree that if there is one thing we learned from the pandemic lockdown, it's how much we missed going to restaurants–especially if you're the one responsible for the meals at home.

Eating seafood and waterfront dining are Sarasota, Florida must-do food experiences, and there are plenty of opportunities to indulge in both.

Florida's coastal waters offer abundant fishing, and there are even restaurants that will cook your catch. But you can enjoy fresh seafood without heading out on a boat yourself. You'll find off-the-boat fresh seafood on most restaurant menus. Here are three favorites among residents and visitors alike.

Shrimp: Did you know nearly 85% of the shrimp in the US come from the west coast of Florida? The Fort Myers Beach shrimping fleet is the largest commercial fishing fleet in the Gulf. One of the tastiest shrimp species you can find is the Key West Pink Shrimp, prized for its sweet, mild flavor and tender meat. Key West Pinks live in clean coral sand off the west coast of Florida and are caught year-round but especially abundant from November through June. Insider tip – Airport security allows you to carry packaged shrimp, and seafood markets will flash-freeze shrimp for travel!

Stone Crab: Stone crab has a sweet flavor with a firm, flaky texture and is often compared to lobster. It is typically served cold with drawn butter and lemon, cocktail sauces, mayonnaises, or vinaigrettes. Stone crab is only available October 15 – May 1, and I promise they're worth every penny.

Grouper: This mild white fish has a subtle sweet flavor and firm texture. It is delicious grilled, fried, baked, or sautéed. You'll find grouper tacos and grouper sandwiches widely available on local menus.

One of the major perks about living in Florida is that we have year-round favorable weather, perfect for outdoor dining. Kick your alfresco dinner options up a notch with a sunset picnic on the beach! There's just something about toes in the sand dining. The sound of softly crashing waves or lapping water and gentle blowing breezes create a memorable atmosphere.

For an easy-peasy picnic, order take out from a restaurant or visit a local grocery to pick up finger foods or snacks and something to drink. Specialty grocers like Crescent Beach Grocery and Morton's offer a wide array of food options from ready-made meals to deli salads, sandwiches, gourmet cheeses, nuts, fresh fruit, and crudité. Plus, they have wine and beer!

Pack a cooler, beach blanket or chairs, your camera, some beach toys for the kids, and head to the beach with family or friends. Be sure to include a flashlight if you plan to stay after dark.

If picnics just aren't your thing or you prefer to let someone else do all the work, then a lunch, dinner, or sunset cruise is an excellent dine on the water option.

Nita Ettinger is the co-publisher for Siesta Publications and Editor in Chief for Must Do Visitor Guides. Must Do Visitor Guides provides Southwest Florida visitor information through printed publications and the website MustDo.com. Must Do Visitor Guides are published bi-annually and are available at no cost in Sarasota, Lee and Collier County chambers of commerce, visitor information centers, select Southwest Florida hotels and wherever free publications are found.

O'LEARY'S TIKI BAR & GRILL
5 Bayfront Drive
941-953-7505
olearystikibar.com

DOWNTOWN	AMERICAN	COST: $$

HOURS: Sun-Thur, 8AM to 10PM • Fri & Sat, 8AM to 11PM

WHAT TO EXPECT: Live music • Beach bar • Cold beer
Great views • Watersports rentals

CARRYOUT/DELIVERY INFO: Full menu available for carryout. No phone-in ordering. Must order carryout at the restaurant. Delivery not available.

SCAN FOR MENU

SOME BASICS
Reservations:	NO
Spirits:	FULL BAR
Parking:	LOT
Outdoor Dining:	YES

OPHELIA'S ON THE BAY
9105 Midnight Pass Road
941-349-2212
opheliasonthebay.net

SIESTA KEY	AMERICAN	COST: $$$

HOURS: Dinner Nightly, 5PM to 10PM

WHAT TO EXPECT: Great for a date • Nice water view
Good wine list • OpenTable reservations

CARRYOUT/DELIVERY INFO: Full menu available for carryout. Curbside pick up. Delivery not available.

SCAN FOR MENU

SOME BASICS
Reservations:	YES
Spirits:	FULL BAR
Parking:	VALET
Outdoor Dining:	YES

ORIGIN CRAFT BEER & PIZZA CAFÉ

1837 Hillview Street*
941-316-9222
originpizzacafe.com

SOUTHSIDE VILLAGE	PIZZA	COST: $$

HOURS: Sun-Thur, 11AM to 1AM • Fri & Sat, 11AM to 2AM

WHAT TO EXPECT: Neighborhood feel • Open late • Friendly staff
Local favorite • New (2020) 2nd location • Craft beer

CARRYOUT/DELIVERY INFO: Full menu available for carryout
and delivery. Curbside and contactless pick up. Delivery available
through Bite Squad, Uber Eats and Grubhub.

SCAN FOR MENU

SOME BASICS

Reservations:	NO
Spirits:	BEER/WINE
Parking:	LOT/STREET
Outdoor Dining:	YES

THE OVERTON

1420 Boulevard of the Arts
941-552-6927
theovertonsrq.com

ROSEMARY DISTRICT	AMERICAN	COST: $$

HOURS: Tue-Sun, 8AM to 7PM
CLOSED MONDAY

WHAT TO EXPECT: Super casual • Good for a meet-up
Specialty coffee

CARRYOUT/DELIVERY INFO: Full menu available for carryout.
Delivery not available.

SCAN FOR INFO

SOME BASICS

Reservations:	NONE
Spirits:	BEER/WINE
Parking:	STREET/LOT
Outdoor Dining:	YES

OWEN'S FISH CAMP

516 Burns Court
941-951-6936
owensfishcamp.com

BURNS COURT	SEAFOOD	COST: $$

HOURS: Daily, 4PM to 9PM

WHAT TO EXPECT: Fun dining experience • Good for families
Busy in season • Parking can be a challenge

CARRYOUT/DELIVERY INFO: Carryout on a limited basis. No curbside or contactless pick up options. Call ahead to restaurant to see if carryout is available. Delivery not available.

SCAN FOR MENU

SOME BASICS

Reservations:	NO
Spirits:	FULL BAR
Parking:	STREET/LOT
Outdoor Dining:	YES

PACIFIC RIM

1859 Hillview Street
941-330-8071
pacrimsrq.com

SOUTHSIDE VILLAGE	ASIAN	COST: $$

HOURS: Mon-Fri, 11:30AM to 2PM • Mon-Thur, 5PM to 9:30PM
Fri & Sat, 5PM to 10:30PM • Sun, 5PM to 9PM

WHAT TO EXPECT: Fun dining experience • Sushi & more
Parking usually available • Happy Hour

CARRYOUT/DELIVERY INFO: Full menu available for carryout and delivery. Curbside pick up. Delivery through Bite Squad.

SCAN FOR MENU

SOME BASICS

Reservations:	4 OR MORE
Spirits:	FULL BAR
Parking:	LOT/STREET
Outdoor Dining:	YES

THE PARROT PATIO BAR & GRILL
3602 Webber Street
941-952-3352
theparrotpatiobar.com

AMERICAN	COST: $$

HOURS: Mon-Thur, 11AM to 11PM • Fri & Sat, 11AM to 12AM
Happy Hour, Mon-Fri, 11:30 to 7PM

WHAT TO EXPECT: Very casual • Sports bar feel • LIVE music
NFL football package • Good for groups

CARRYOUT/DELIVERY INFO: Online ordering available. Full menu available for carryout. Curbside pick up. Delivery not available.

SCAN FOR MENU

SOME BASICS
Reservations:	NO
Spirits:	FULL BAR
Parking:	LOT
Outdoor Dining:	YES

PASTRY ART
1512 Main Street
941-955-7545
pastryartbakerycafe.com

DOWNTOWN	AMERICAN	COST: $$

HOURS: Mon-Thur, 7AM to 7PM • Fri & Sat, 7AM to 10PM
Sun, 8AM to 5PM

WHAT TO EXPECT: Great for a coffee date • Live music
Wi-Fi • Busy weekend spot

CARRYOUT/DELIVERY INFO: Full menu available for carryout and delivery. Delivery available until 2PM. Delivery is through the restaurant.

SCAN FOR MENU

SOME BASICS
Reservations:	NO
Spirits:	BEER/WINE
Parking:	STREET
Outdoor Dining:	YES

PATRICK'S 1481

1481 Main Street
941-955-1481
patricks1481.com

DOWNTOWN	AMERICAN	COST: $$

HOURS: Sun, 11:30AM to 9PM • Mon, 11:30AM to 10PM
Tue-Thur, 11:30AM to 9PM • Fri & Sat, 11:30AM to 10PM

WHAT TO EXPECT: Sat. & Sun. brunch • Local favorite
Good Happy Hour

CARRYOUT/DELIVERY INFO: Online ordering available. Full menu
available for carryout and delivery. Delivery available
through DoorDash.

SCAN FOR MENU

SOME BASICS

Reservations:	5 OR MORE
Spirits:	FULL BAR
Parking:	STREET/VALET
Outdoor Dining:	YES

PAZZO SOUTHSIDE

1936 Hillview Street
941-260-8831
pazzosouthside.com

SOUTHSIDE VILLAGE	ITALIAN	COST: $$

HOURS: Mon-Thur, 11AM to 9PM • Fri, 11AM to 10PM
Sat, 5PM to 10PM • CLOSED SUNDAY

WHAT TO EXPECT: Good for a date • Pizza
Bar for solo diners • New location (2020)

CARRYOUT/DELIVERY INFO: Online ordering available. Special
carryout menu. Curbside and contactless pick up.
Delivery not available.

SCAN FOR MENU

SOME BASICS

Reservations:	YES
Spirits:	BEER/WINE
Parking:	LOT/STREET
Outdoor Dining:	YES

Food Trucks are popular. And, just like every other great food community, we've got our share roaming the streets. Here's a little basic info to help you navigate through the maze of local mobile dining options. These are a few of our favorites!

HAMLET'S EATERY
What They Serve: Tacos and slider boxes. Both meat and vegan options are available.
Where You Can Find Them:
The Bazaar on Apricot & Lime
Info at: hamletseatery.com

MOBSTAH LOBSTAH
What They Serve: "Seafood to die for!" Serving up Maine lobster rolls and a whole lot more.
Where You Can Find Them:
Calusa Brewing, various area seafood events.
Info at: mobstahlobstah.com or FB Page

MOUTHOLE BBQ
What They Serve: BBQ, BBQ, AND BBQ. Beef, pork, ribs, and chicken. Also some great desserts.
Where You Can Find Them: Various locations around the Sarasota area. Check their Facebook page for details.
Info at: moutholebbq.com

SIMPLY GREEK BY WYNNBERRY
What They Serve: Authentic Greek cuisine in a food truck! Gyros, moussaka and more. Try the Greek fries.
Where You Can Find Them:
Various stops around the Sarasota area.
Info at: simplygreekbywynnberry.com

PHILLPPI CREEK OYSTER BAR

5353 South Tamiami Trail
941-925-4444
creekseafood.com

SOUTH TRAIL	SEAFOOD	COST: $$

HOURS: Sun-Thur, 11AM to 9PM • Fri & Sat, 11AM to 9PM

WHAT TO EXPECT: Great for families • Water view • Casual dining
Busy during season • Good for kids

CARRYOUT/DELIVERY INFO: Full menu available for carryout.
Curbside pick up. Delivery not available.

SCAN FOR MENU

SOME BASICS
Reservations:	NO
Spirits:	FULL BAR
Parking:	LOT
Outdoor Dining:	YES

PHO CALI

1578 Main Street
941-955-2683
phocalisarasota.com

DOWNTOWN	VIETNAMESE	COST: $

HOURS: Mon-Thur, 11AM to 9PM • Fri & Sat, 11AM to 9:30PM
CLOSED SUNDAY

WHAT TO EXPECT: Great service • Casual dining
Easy on the wallet • Good for families • Noodle bowls!

CARRYOUT/DELIVERY INFO: Full menu available for carryout.
Delivery not available.

SCAN FOR MENU

SOME BASICS
Reservations:	NO
Spirits:	BEER/WINE
Parking:	STREET
Outdoor Dining:	NO

PICCOLO ITALIAN MARKET & DELI
6518 Gateway Avenue
941-923-2202
piccolomarket.com

GULF GATE	ITALIAN	COST: $

HOURS: Tue-Fri, 10AM to 6PM • Sat, 10AM to 4PM
CLOSED SUNDAY

WHAT TO EXPECT: Great for a quick lunch • Italian market
Super casual • Delicious sandwiches • Catering available

CARRYOUT/DELIVERY INFO: Online ordering available. Full menu available for carryout and delivery. Curbside and contactless pick up. Delivery through DoorDash.

SCAN FOR MENU

SOME BASICS
Reservations:	NO
Spirits:	NONE
Parking:	LOT
Outdoor Dining:	NO

PIER 22
1200 1st Avenue West
941-748-8087
pier22dining.com

BRADENTON	SEAFOOD	COST: $$$

HOURS: Mon-Thur, 11:30AM to 10PM • Fri, 11:30AM to 10:30PM
Sat, 8AM to 10:30PM • Sun, 8AM to 10PM

WHAT TO EXPECT: Great for a date • Water view • Good wine list
OpenTable reservations • Weekend brunch

CARRYOUT/DELIVERY INFO: Online ordering available. Full menu available for carryout. Curbside and contactless pick up. Delivery not available.

SCAN FOR MENU

SOME BASICS
Reservations:	YES
Spirits:	FULL BAR
Parking:	LOT
Outdoor Dining:	YES

PIZZA N' BREW

1507 Main Street*
941-259-3894
pizzanbrew.com

DOWNTOWN	PIZZA	COST: $$

HOURS: Sun-Thur 11AM to 2AM
Fri & Sat, 11AM to 3AM

WHAT TO EXPECT: Late night spot • Casual pizza and beer
Downtown & Siesta Key locations

CARRYOUT/DELIVERY INFO: Full menu available for carryout.
Delivery available through Uber Eats, Grubhub, DoorDash, and
Bite Squad.

SCAN FOR MENU

SOME BASICS

Reservations:	NO
Spirits:	BEER/WINE
Parking:	STREET
Outdoor Dining:	NO

THE POINT

131 Bayview Drive
941-786-3890
eviesonline.com/location/the-point

OSPREY	SEAFOOD	COST: $$

HOURS: Daily, 11AM to 10PM

WHAT TO EXPECT: Three floors of dining • Great Gulf views
Good for groups and parties • Arrive by boat!

CARRYOUT/DELIVERY INFO: Full menu available for carryout.
Delivery not available.

SCAN FOR MENU

SOME BASICS

Reservations:	YES
Spirits:	FULL BAR
Parking:	LOT
Outdoor Dining:	YES

POPPO'S TAQUERIA

4990 South Tamiami Trail
941-343-2341
poppostaqueria.com/location/the-landings

THE LANDINGS	MEXICAN	COST: $$

HOURS: Daily, 11AM to 8PM

WHAT TO EXPECT: Fast casual Mexican cuisine • Easy lunch
Good for families • Lots of parking

CARRYOUT/DELIVERY INFO: Carryout and delivery available.
Delivery through DoorDash and Uber Eats.

SCAN FOR MENU

SOME BASICS

Reservations:	NO
Spirits:	NONE
Parking:	LOT
Outdoor Dining:	YES

POP'S SUNSET GRILL

112 Circuit Road (ICW Marker 10 by boat)
941-488-3177
popssunsetgrill.com

NOKOMIS	SEAFOOD	COST: $$

HOURS: Daily, 11AM to 10PM

WHAT TO EXPECT: Drive thru "Pontiki" food & bev pickup for boats
Water view • Vacation atmosphere • Great for families

CARRYOUT/DELIVERY INFO: Most menu items available
for carryout and delivery. Curbside and dockside pick up.
Contactless pick up. Delivery through DoorDash.

SCAN FOR MENU

SOME BASICS

Reservations:	YES
Spirits:	FULL BAR
Parking:	LOT
Outdoor Dining:	YES

Make it at
HOME

Karaage Chicken Bao Bun
Chef Ken Lumpkin, Kojo

INGREDIENTS
4 medium chicken thighs, boneless, skin on
4 bao buns, available at any Asian market

Brine
1 gallon of cold filtered water
1 cup kosher salt
½ cup light brown sugar

Brine chicken for at least 20 minutes, preferably overnight.

Karaage Marinade
2 cups low sodium soy sauce
1 cup fresh ginger, peeled and minced
¼ cup garlic, peeled and chopped

Place all ingredients in a blender, blend until smooth and
emulsified. Place chicken thighs in marinade, marinate 1-3 hours.

Condiments
Citrus-pepper aioli, kimchi pickles, shredded cabbage

Citrus-Pepper Aioli
1 ½ cup Kewpie mayo
1/8 cup lemon/lime juice mixed 1 to 1
Zest of half orange
1/8 tsp cracked black pepper

Mix all ingredients together.

Kimchi Pickles
4 Persian pickles or 1 European cucumber
½ small head of cabbage

1 tbsp kosher salt
¼ cup Rice wine vinegar
2 tbsp bottled kimchi seasoning
¼ tsp sugar

METHOD
Slice cucumber ¼" thick, toss with salt, let sit for 3 minutes. Transfer to a sieve and let drain for 10 minutes. Rinse with water after 10 minutes and squeeze out excess water. Combine the remaining ingredients in a separate mixing bowl. Whisk until sugar is dissolved. Toss cucumbers in mixture store in an airtight container in the refrigerator.
Cut cabbage into quarters and cut out the core. Shred the cabbage with a mandolin or slice very thin.

Dredge
1 cup Japanese potato starch
1 cup sweet potato starch
Mix both ingredients together.

METHOD
Bring oil, ½ inch depth, to medium heat in a high wall pan (not a pot). Remove chicken thighs from marinade. Toss in dredge and coat generously. Gently place the chicken in the hot oil maintaining medium to medium high heat. Cook 5-7 minutes on each side, should reach an internal temperature of 160-165 degrees.

Remove chicken from oil and let drain on a drip rack. Bring water to a boil. Steam buns in a bamboo steamer lined with cabbage leaves as not to stick. You can steam in a colander lined with cabbage that sits in the pot but does not touch the water. Place the top of the pot on the colander. Steam for 2-3 minutes.

BUILD
Buns should be pre folded, place the chicken in the buns. Drizzle mayo on the chicken, top with shredded cabbage. Top with 2-3 sliced pickles each.

Kojo is located at the Palm Avenue Garage in downtown Sarasota, 1289 N. Palm Avenue. Serving a menu of modern Asian cuisine and a fantastic selection of premium sake. For reservations call, (941) 536- 9717 or eatkojo.com.

PUB 32
8383 South Tamiami Trail
941-952-3070
pub32sarasota.com

SOUTH TRAIL	IRISH	COST: $$

HOURS: Tue-Sun, 12PM to 9PM • CLOSED MONDAY

WHAT TO EXPECT: Great casual dining • Good beer list
Live music • Monday night whiskey club

CARRYOUT/DELIVERY INFO: Full menu available for carryout and
delivery. Curbside pick up. Delivery available through Bite Squad.

SCAN FOR MENU

SOME BASICS

Reservations:	YES
Spirits:	FULL BAR
Parking:	LOT
Outdoor Dining:	YES

THE PUBLIC HOUSE

`NEW`

6240 North Lockwood Ridge Road
941-822-0795
the-public-house.com

	AMERICAN	COST: $$

HOURS: Sun-Thur 11AM to 9PM
Fri & Sat, 11AM to 10PM

WHAT TO EXPECT: Burgers, pizza and more • Lots of parking
Online ordering • Super casual atmosphere

CARRYOUT/DELIVERY INFO: Full menu available for carryout and
delivery. Delivery available through Uber Eats, Grubhub, and
DoorDash.

SCAN FOR MENU

SOME BASICS

Reservations:	NO
Spirits:	FULL BAR
Parking:	LOT
Outdoor Dining:	NO

RASOI INDIAN KITCHEN
7119 South Tamiami Trail
941-921-9200
rasoisarasota.com

SOUTH TRAIL	INDIAN	COST: $$

HOURS: Lunch, Tue-Fri, 11AM to 3PM • Sat & Sun, 11AM to 3:30PM
Dinner, Tue-Sun , 5PM to 10PM • CLOSED MONDAY

WHAT TO EXPECT: Upscale, but, casual dining • Lots of parking
Authentic Indian Cuisine

CARRYOUT/DELIVERY INFO: Full menu available for carryout and
delivery. Curbside pick up. Delivery available through Bite Squad,
Uber Eats, DoorDash and Grubhub.

SCAN FOR MENU

SOME BASICS
Reservations:	YES
Spirits:	BEER/WINE
Parking:	LOT
Outdoor Dining:	NO

REEF CAKES
1812 South Osprey Avenue
941-444-7968
reefcakes.com

SOUTHSIDE VILLAGE	SEAFOOD	COST: $$

HOURS: Tues-Fri, 11AM to 9PM • Sat, 3PM to 9PM
CLOSED SUNDAY & MONDAY

WHAT TO EXPECT: Fish Cakes • Casual dining experience

CARRYOUT/DELIVERY INFO: Full menu available for carryout.
Curbside and contactless pick up available. Delivery available
through DoorDash, Uber Eats and Bite Squad.

SCAN FOR INFO

SOME BASICS
Reservations:	NO
Spirits:	BEER/WINE
Parking:	STREET
Outdoor Dining:	NO

RENDEZ-VOUS FRENCH BAKERY

5336 Clark Road*
941-924-1234
rendezvoussarasota.com

	FRENCH	COST: $$

HOURS: Tues-Sat, 7:30AM to 3PM • Sun, 8AM to 3PM
CLOSED MONDAY

WHAT TO EXPECT: Fresh French baked goods • Catering
Fantastic French omelets! • Very casual

CARRYOUT/DELIVERY INFO: Full menu available for carryout.
Curbside pick up. Delivery not available.

SCAN FOR MENU

SOME BASICS
Reservations:	NO
Spirits:	NONE
Parking:	LOT
Outdoor Dining:	YES

REYNA'S TAQUERIA

935 North Beneva Road (Sarasota Commons)
941-260-8343
reynastaqueria.com

SARASOTA COMMONS	MEXICAN	COST: $

HOURS: Sun-Thur, 11AM to 8PM • Fri & Sat, 11AM to 10PM

WHAT TO EXPECT: Family friendly • Super easy on the wallet
Lots of parking • Authentic Mexican cuisine

CARRYOUT/DELIVERY INFO: Full menu available for carryout
and delivery. Curbside and contactless pick up. Delivery available
through Bite Squad and Uber Eats.

SCAN FOR MENU

SOME BASICS
Reservations:	NO
Spirits:	BEER/WINE
Parking:	LOT
Outdoor Dining:	NO

RICO'S PIZZERIA
1902 Bay Road
941-366-8988
ricospizzapie.com

ITALIAN	COST: $$

HOURS: Sun-Thur & Sat, 11AM to 10PM • Fri, 11AM to 11PM

WHAT TO EXPECT: Family pizza place • Italian specialty dishes
Sandwiches • Casual dining experience

CARRYOUT/DELIVERY INFO: Online ordering. Full menu available
for carryout and delivery. Curbside and contactless pick up.
Delivery available through restaurant.

SCAN FOR MENU

SOME BASICS
Reservations:	NO
Spirits:	BEER/WINE
Parking:	LOT
Outdoor Dining:	NO

RIPFIRE PIZZA & BBQ
5218 Ocean Boulevard
941-313-7511
ripfirepizza.com

SIESTA KEY	PIZZA	COST: $$

HOURS: Daily, 11AM to 10PM

WHAT TO EXPECT: Fast fired pizza • In the heart Siesta Village
Good craft beer selection • Family friendly

CARRYOUT/DELIVERY INFO: Full menu available for carryout and
delivery. Delivery available through Slice.

SCAN FOR MENU

SOME BASICS
Reservations:	NO
Spirits:	BEER/WINE
Parking:	STREET
Outdoor Dining:	YES

BEER
Sarasota's Best

Craft beer, brew pubs, and full on local breweries. Sarasota is not immune from the small batch beer craze. As a matter of fact, we've got some damn good beer craftsmen right here in town. Oh, and along with these local artisans are some great places to down a few unique brews. Here's a list of some of our local favorites. - Cheers!

SARASOTA BREWERIES & BREWPUBS

BIG TOP BREWING
975 Cattlemen Road
Sarasota, FL 34232
941-371-2939
bigtopbrewing.com

BREW LIFE BREWING
5765 S Beneva Road
Sarasota, FL 34233
941-952-3831
brewlifebrewing.com

CALUSA BREWING
5701 Derek Avenue
Sarasota, FL 34233
941-922-8150
calusabrewing.com

DARWIN BREWING COMPANY
803 7th Avenue W
Bradenton, FL 34205
941-747-1970
darwinbrewingco.com

MOTORWORKS BREWING
1014 9th Street W
Bradenton, FL 34205
941-567-6218
motorworksbrewing.com

SARASOTA BREWING COMPANY
6607 Gateway Avenue
Sarasota, FL 34231
941-925-2337
sarasotabrewing.com

SARASOTA BEER BARS

MANDEVILLE BEER GARDEN
428 N. Lemon Avenue
Sarasota, FL 34236
941-954-8688
mandevillebeergarden.com

99 BOTTLES
1445 2nd Street
Sarasota, FL 34236
941-487-7874
99bottles.net

SHAMROCK PUB
2257 Ringling Boulevard
Sarasota, FL 34237
941-952-1730
shamrocksarasota.com

Please Drink Responsibly

ROESSLER'S
2033 Vamo Way
941-966-5688
roesslersrestaurant.com

SOUTH TRAIL	EUROPEAN	COST: $$$

HOURS: Dinner, Tues-Sun, 5PM to close
CLOSED MONDAY

WHAT TO EXPECT: Good wine list • Private dining room
Family owned & operated since 1978 • Online reservations

CARRYOUT/DELIVERY INFO: Full menu available for carryout.
Curbside pick up. Delivery not available.

SCAN FOR MENU

SOME BASICS
Reservations:	YES
Spirits:	FULL BAR
Parking:	LOT
Outdoor Dining:	YES

ROMANSQ
6670 Superior Avenue
941-237-8742
romansq.com

NEW

GULF GATE	PIZZA	COST: $$

HOURS: Thur-Sat, 3PM to 8PM
CLOSED SUNDAY-WEDNESDAY

WHAT TO EXPECT: "Roman" style pizza • Fresh baked bread
Online ordering

CARRYOUT/DELIVERY INFO: Full menu available for carryout and
delivery. Delivery available through cake.net.

SCAN FOR MENU

SOME BASICS
Reservations:	NO
Spirits:	NONE
Parking:	LOT/STREET
Outdoor Dining:	NO

ROSEBUD'S STEAKHOUSE & SEAFOOD

2215 South Tamiami Trail
941-918-8771
rosebudssarasota.com

OSPREY	STEAKHOUSE	COST: $$$

HOURS: Tues-Sun, 4PM to 10PM
CLOSED MONDAY

WHAT TO EXPECT: Early bird dining • Private dining room
Aged, hand cut, Angus steaks • Established 1995

CARRYOUT/DELIVERY INFO: Online ordering. Full menu available
for carryout. Curbside and contactless pick up.
Delivery not available.

SCAN FOR MENU

SOME BASICS
Reservations:	YES
Spirits:	FULL BAR
Parking:	LOT
Outdoor Dining:	NO

THE ROSEMARY

411 North Orange Avenue
941-955-7600
therosemarysarasota.com

ROSEMARY DISTRICT	AMERICAN	COST: $$

HOURS: Daily, 8AM to 2PM

WHAT TO EXPECT: Casual dining • Busy in season
Downtown, north of Fruitville • Nice lunch spot

CARRYOUT/DELIVERY INFO: Full menu available for carryout.
Please call the restaurant for delivery options.

SCAN FOR MENU

SOME BASICS
Reservations:	YES
Spirits:	BEER/WINE
Parking:	STREET
Outdoor Dining:	YES

ROSEMARY AND THYME

511 North Orange Avenue
941-955-7600
therosemarysarasota.com

| ROSEMARY DISTRICT | AMERICAN | COST: $$$ |

HOURS: Wed-Sat 4:30PM to 9PM

WHAT TO EXPECT: Upscale, but, casual • OpenTable reservations
Great appetizers • Don't forget dessert

CARRYOUT/DELIVERY INFO: Special three-course carryout
menu available. Full menu also available for carryout.
Delivery not available.

SCAN FOR INFO

SOME BASICS
Reservations:	YES
Spirits:	FULL BAR
Parking:	STREET
Outdoor Dining:	NO

SAGE

1216 First Street
941-445-5660
sagesrq.com

| DOWNTOWN | AMERICAN | COST: $$$ |

HOURS: Tues-Thur, 5PM to 10PM
Fri & Sat, 5PM to 11PM

WHAT TO EXPECT: Upscale dining • Private event space
OpenTable reservations • Rooftop is great for a date

CARRYOUT/DELIVERY INFO: Full menu available for carryout.
Curbside pick up. Delivery not available.

SCAN FOR MENU

SOME BASICS
Reservations:	YES
Spirits:	FULL BAR
Parking:	LOT/STREET
Outdoor Dining:	YES

THE SANDBAR
100 Spring Avenue
941-778-0444
sandbardining.com

ANNA MARIA	AMERICAN	COST: $$

HOURS: Mon-Thur, 11:30AM to 9PM • Fri & Sat, 11:30AM to 10PM
Sun, 10AM to 9PM

WHAT TO EXPECT: Great causal beach dining • Island feel
Good for a private beach party

CARRYOUT/DELIVERY INFO: Online ordering available. Full menu
available for carryout. Delivery not available.

SCAN FOR MENU

SOME BASICS

Reservations:	NO
Spirits:	FULL BAR
Parking:	LOT
Outdoor Dining:	YES

Scan for the latest Sarasota
Restaurant news.
Subscribe to our newsletter

sarasota bites

on Bulletin

SARASOTA BREWING COMPANY

6607 Gateway Avenue
941-925-2337
sarasotabrewing.com

GULF GATE	AMERICAN	COST: $$

HOURS: Mon-Thur, 11AM to 8PM • Fri & Sat, 11AM to 10PM
Sun, 11PM to 8PM

WHAT TO EXPECT: Craft brewpub • Established 1989
Chicago style pizza & beef sandwiches • Good for sports

CARRYOUT/DELIVERY INFO: Full menu available for carryout
and delivery. Curbside and contactless pick up. Delivery available
through Bite Squad.

SCAN FOR MENU

SOME BASICS

Reservations:	YES
Spirits:	BEER/WINE
Parking:	LOT
Outdoor Dining:	NO

SARDINIA

5770 South Tamiami Trail
941-702-8582
sardiniasrq.com

SOUTH TRAIL	ITALIAN	COST: $$$

HOURS: Mon-Sat, 5PM to 10PM
CLOSED SUNDAY

WHAT TO EXPECT: Small & intimate dining • Homemade dishes
Private dining room available • Chef driven menu

CARRYOUT/DELIVERY INFO: Full menu available for carryout.
Delivery available through DoorDash.

SCAN FOR MENU

SOME BASICS

Reservations:	YES
Spirits:	BEER/WINE
Parking:	LOT
Outdoor Dining:	NO

SCHNITZEL KITCHEN

6521 Superior Avenue
941-922-9299
sites.google.com/view/schnitzelsrq/home

GULF GATE	GERMAN	COST: $$

HOURS: Tues-Sat, 4PM to 9PM
CLOSED SUNDAY & MONDAY

WHAT TO EXPECT: Casual ethnic cuisine • Homemade dishes
BIG German beer selection

CARRYOUT/DELIVERY INFO: Full menu available for carryout and delivery. Curbside pick up. Delivery available through Bite Squad and DoorDash.

SCAN FOR MENU

SOME BASICS

Reservations:	YES
Spirits:	BEER & WINE
Parking:	LOT/STREET
Outdoor Dining:	NO

SCREAMING GOAT TAQUERIA

6606 Superior Avenue
941-210-3992
screaming-goat.com

GULF GATE	MEXICAN	COST: $

HOURS: Mon-Sat, 11AM to 8PM • CLOSED SUNDAY

WHAT TO EXPECT: Super casual • Taco shack • Family friendly
Great for a quick lunch or dinner

CARRYOUT/DELIVERY INFO: Online ordering available. Full menu available for carryout and delivery. Delivery available through Uber Eats.

SCAN FOR MENU

SOME BASICS

Reservations:	NONE
Spirits:	BEER/WINE
Parking:	LOT/STREET
Outdoor Dining:	NO

Your Beer Drinking
STYLE GUIDE

By Ed Paulsen, Certified Cicerone®

"What are you in the mood for?" It's my first and favorite question when greeting a customer. This simple variant on "what can I get you?" tends to prompt conversation as well as underline the ever-expanding options available for the curious drinker.

Given this wonderful, often bewildering, range of choices we are left to ask ourselves, "Well, what flavors am I craving? What type of experience do I want? Something buoyant or thought-provoking? Full and smooth or clean and brisk?"

With the aim of satisfying both your thirst and curiosity, I would like to present the following selected list of beer styles. Included are some suggestions for excellent examples, as well as some information on gluten-free/reduced and mead.

Abbey Ale
Most associated with the Belgian monastic brewing traditions, there are some fine US examples, as well. Expect medium-to-high strength and effervescence with notes of spice and dark fruits. These beers pair well with food and are appropriately worthy of contemplation. Examples: St. Bernardus, Leffe, Affligem. See: Trappist, Dubbel, Tripel

Berliner Weisse
Berlin's famous wheat beer, traditionally served with an herb or fruit syrup on the side. Light, sparkling with an

appetizing tartness, it is a popular base style for playful American interpretations. Examples: Bell's Oarsman Ale, Big Top Ringmaster Raspberry. See: Wheat Beer

Bock
Originating in the mid-north of Einbeck in Lower Saxony, Bocks are the famed rich, strong lagers of Bavaria. Often associated with spring (Maibock) or Lent (Doppelbock). American versions such as Shiner Bock, Genessee Bock, Anheuser-Busch Amberbock, tend to be modest, yet flavorful, amber lagers. Examples: Ayinger Celebrator, Paulaner Salvator

Brown Ale
Associated with the Northeast of England, brown ales are full of flavor; malty, lightly roasty or chocolatey, and with a solid drinkability. American examples often stronger and may have a pronounced hop character in aroma and/or finish. Examples: Cigar City Maduro, Bell's Best Brown Ale, Newcastle Brown Ale

Dubbel
A Belgian abbey-style ale of deep mahogany, usually around 7% ABV. Very expressive flavors of dark fruits and spice on account of unique yeast strains. Excellent food-pairing beers. Examples: Westmalle Dubbel, Chimay Red, Ommegang Abbey Ale See: Abbey Styles, Trappist

Flanders Red/Brown Ale
"The Burgundies of Belgium" these oak-aged vinous, tart ales are among the world's most unique, delicious, and genre-bending. Pairing amazingly with food and even cooking as an ingredient in the famous Carbonnades Flamandes (Flemish beef stew). Examples: Rodenbach Grand Cru, Duchess De Bourgogne, New Belgium La Folie

Framboise

Pronounced 'fram-BWAHZ', a variety of Belgian Lambic with raspberry. For many, synonymous with Lindemans, a fine and widely available producer of a range of Lambic beers. Served in a striking fluted glass, Framboise is a classic aperitif and surprisingly good with chocolate desserts. Examples: Lindemans Framboise.
See: Lambic

Gluten-Free Beers

Gluten-free beers are most often made with millet, sorghum or other grains and are the right choices for Celiac Diet or those avoiding gluten entirely. Gluten-reduced beers are brewed and fermented as standard beers later having an enzyme added that breaks the gluten into its constituent parts and are suitable for those with thyroid-related conditions or other sensitivities. Many beers in both categories are made in a wide variety of styles with excellent quality.
Gluten-free examples: Ghost Fish, Lakefront New Grist, Glutenberg
Gluten-reduced examples: Omission by Widmer, Stone Delicious IPA, Two Brothers

Gose

Pronounced 'GO-zuh', a German wheat beer of low to mid-strength with a refreshing tartness, interestingly spiced with coriander seed and salt. Another playful canvas for experimentation and flattering for certain types of fruit additions. Examples: Anderson Valley Gose, Dogfish Seaquench. See: Wheat Beer, Berliner Weisse

Hefeweizen

Historically enjoyed by Bavarian royalty, Hefeweizen is the famous cloudy wheat beer of Germany. With an expressive fermentation character of spice and clove,

it is traditionally served in a tall glass with a grand cap of foam. Examples: Franziskaner, Erdinger, Paulaner, Widmer, Sierra Nevada Kellerweiss
See: Wheat Beer

Imperial Stout
Strongest of the stout family historically produced for export to the Russian court in the 18th century. Roasty, full-bodied, with deep notes of dark chocolate and espresso. A strong candidate for barrel aging and currently often a welcome playground for dessert-like additions (vanilla, chocolate, coconut)
Examples: Sierra Nevada Narwhal, Cigar City Marshal Zhukov, North Coast Old Rasputin
See: Stout, Porter

International Lager
Balanced and familiar, some version of this pale lager exists in nearly every country in the world. Rooted in the classic golden lagers of Europe, International Lager is a safe and solid standby. Examples: Heineken Tsing Tao, Kingfisher, Kronenberg, Stella Artois
See: Pilsner, Lager

IPA
Originating in Britain, this style has come to embody modern American craft beer more than any other. An enthusiastic and occasionally unapologetic celebration of the flavors and aromas of the wonderful hop. American versions may be explosively aromatic with notes of citrus, pine, and even tropical fruits. The 'hazy' style that originated in the Northeast US within the last decade features a softer mouthfeel and sense of 'juiciness'
Examples: Cigar City Jai Alai, Calusa Zote, Stone IPA, Bells Two-Hearted, Founders All Day IPA, Big Top Ashely Gang

Kolsch

The famous beer of Cologne traditionally served in thin, narrow glasses called Stange ("rod"). Straw gold with a refreshing character and slight fruitiness from a cool-fermenting ale strain unique to the style. American versions often unsurprisingly have more hop character in either aroma, bitterness, or both. Examples: Reissdorf, Gaffel, Sierra Nevada

Lager

Not a style, but a family of beers and type of fermentation historically associated with Germany, Denmark, and what is now the Czech Republic. Of a wide range of colors, strengths, and flavors, great lager beers express the very essence of malt, hops, and drinkability with a generally a more neutral fermentation character. Examples of lager styles include Pilsner, Oktoberfest/Marzen, Dark Lager, Bock, Vienna Lager, Schwarzbier and others.

Lambic

One of the most unique and oldest beer styles in the world, Lambics are a taste of the past and a true expression of craft and terroir. Produced only around Brussels, they harness wild yeast and cultures unique to this area. Years-long aging in huge oak vessels creates beers of astonishing flavor, acidity, and complexity. Traditionally some fruits such as cherry, and more recently raspberry, ,may be added which complement the tart, dry character. Global interpretations of this style can be more playful still, with unconventional fruit additions and even character from the wood itself, as in wine barrels. Examples: Lindemans, Cantillon, Boon (pr. 'bone')

Mead

One of the world's oldest and most revered fermented beverages, mead has been experiencing a resurgence in recent years. Mead can be still or sparkling, dry or sweet, with strengths ranging from the most modest beers to the most powerful wines. Traditionally, mead was often combined with herbs, spices (even hops!), or fruits. With a modern spirit of playfulness, such additions have become even more extreme with creative additions such as tea, vanilla, even peanut butter(!). Naturally gluten-free, mead is a fascinating showcase for local terroir and honey varieties. Examples: Redstone Meadery, Schramm's Mead, Bee Nektar, as well as a range of small and traditional producers.

Oktoberfest/Marzen
A moderately strong, malt-accented amber lager associated with the fall season and Oktoberfest celebration. Traditionally German but popular with American breweries. Examples: Samuel Adams, Hofbrau, Ayinger, Weiheinstephaner

Pale Ale
A balanced, mid-strength ale style of British origin with lean toward hop character. American examples, personified by Sierra Nevada, often have even more hop aroma and flavor with a more neutral malt and fermentation character. Examples: Sierra Nevada, Fuller's London Pride, Oskar Blues Dale's Pale Ale

Pilsner
The world's classic golden lager born in Bohemia in 1842. Dry, aromatic, and appetizing with an herbal, floral hop character and crisp finish, Pilsner is one of the world's great beer styles. Examples: Pilsner Urquell, Bitburger, Green Bench Postcard Pils, Calusa Outbound, Darwin Pirata Pils

Porter

Once one of the world's most popular styles, it flourished in the 18th century as British industry, seafaring and imperialism spread it throughout the world. Nearly extinct in its home country as recently as the 1970's it was revived by American brewers. Today, it is a roasty, balanced beer of mid-strength and character. Stronger versions such as Baltic Porter or Imperial Porter wield much of the power of Imperial Stout but often showcase more chocolatey smoothness over assertive roasted character. Examples: Founders Porter, Fuller's London Porter, Bell's Porter, Sierra Nevada Porter, Deschutes Black Butte

Saison

Typically a golden Belgian Ale with a pronounced fruit/spice character, a noticeable hop character and quenching dryness. In a modern sense, nearly anything Belgian-esqe that doesn't fit too neatly in a box may be described as Saison. Interpretations may be oak-aged or oak-fermented presenting fruity, slightly tart character. May be highly hopped or spiced, light or dark, with or without fruit additions. Examples, Saison Dupont, La Chouffe, Boulevard Tank 7, Jolly Pumpkin Bam Biere and Oro de Calabaza, Fantome, Goose Island Sophie

Stout

Perhaps the quintessential 'dark beer' with a focus on the chocolatey, coffee-like character of roasted grains. A true family of beers, ranging from the light, dry character of Guinness through the intensity of Imperial Stout. Substyles include Oatmeal Stout, Milk/Sweet Stout, Foreign/Tropical stout. Dry and appetizing, Irish Dry Stout is exemplified by Guinness with the crisp, bright character of roasted barley. Examples Left-hand Milk Stout, Deschutes Obsidian Stout, Guinness, Lion Stout
See: Imperial Stout, Porter

Trappist

Not a style per se but a designation of production and origin relating to Trappist Monasteries. Popularly associated with Belgium and brands such as Chimay, most produce a range of Abbey-style ales (Dubbel, Tripel, etc). Examples: Chimay, Rochefort, Orval, Westmalle, La Trappe, Spencer (US)
See: Abbey Ale

Triple/Tripel

A strong, golden beer around 9% ABV originating with the version from Westmalle in Belgium. Many fine craft examples abound, including Victory Brewing's Golden Monkey. Examples: Westmalle Tripel, Chimay White, Victory Golden Monkey, New Belgium Tripel
See: Abbey Ale, Trappist

Wheat Beer

A family of ales containing a portion of wheat in addition to barley, traditionally ranging from the Western coast of Belgium and The Netherlands through Germany and Poland. Generally golden and occasionally gently spiced, they all share a wonderful drinkability and lively carbonation. American examples, such as Bell's Oberon, often lack the spice and fruit character of continental versions.
See: Hefeweizen, Gose, Berliner Weisse, Witbier

Witbier

An ancient style of wheat beer with an expressive fermentation character, and creamy, soft drinkability. Traditionally spiced with coriander seed and orange peel. Examples: Hoegaarden, Allagash White, Blue Moon, Big Top Trapeze Monk
See: Wheat Beer

SARASOTA SUSHI
YOUR BEST ROLLS ROLL HERE!

Looking for sushi in Sarasota? You're going to have a decision to make. We have some fantastic and creative sushi chefs that call Sarasota their home. We've got 20+ places where you can indulge. Space is limited here, so we have personally curated a list of some of the best places in town (subject to debate of course). Whether, you're sitting at the bar or at a table with a group of friends you can't go wrong with any of these places. Oh, just say "OMAKASE" and watch the magic happen...

DaRuMa Japanese Steak House • 5459 Fruitville Rd • 342-6600
WHAT TO EXPECT: Sushi + Teppan tableside cooking. This place is great for groups and big parties. Now open in The Landings.

Drunken Poet Cafe • 1572 Main St. • 955-8404
WHAT TO EXPECT: Sushi + Thai. A large selection of sushi. Downtown location. Also, lots of cooked options to choose from.

Jpan Restaurant • 3800 S. Tamiami Trl. • 954-5726
WHAT TO EXPECT: Always great. Never a miss here. BIG sushi menu. Super creative presentations. Also, across from UTC mall.

Kiyoshi's Sushi • 6550 Gateway Ave. • 924-3781
WHAT TO EXPECT: Nigiri, sashimi, and maki. That's pretty much it. This is a sushi restaurant. Very upscale creations & presentations.

Pacific Rim • 1859 Hillview St. • 330-0218
WHAT TO EXPECT: One of Sarasota's most established sushi restaurants. Good for groups. Lots of cooked dishes too.

Star Thai & Sushi • 240 Avenida Madera • 217-6758
WHAT TO EXPECT: Really creative & well presented sushi dishes. Lots of Thai choices as well. Friendly Siesta Key atmosphere.

Yume Sushi • 1537 Main St. • 363-0604
WHAT TO EXPECT: Downtown's go-to sushi place. Lots & lots of sushi. Also, a big assortment of other options. Great bar, too!

SELVA GRILL

1345 Main Street*
941-362-4427
selvagrill.com

DOWNTOWN	PERUVIAN	COST: $$$

HOURS: Sun-Thur, 5PM to 11PM • Fri & Sat, 5PM to 1AM

WHAT TO EXPECT: Great for a date • Main & Palm
OpenTable reservations

CARRYOUT/DELIVERY INFO: Full menu available for carryout.
Curbside pick up not available. Delivery not available.

SCAN FOR MENU

SOME BASICS
Reservations:	YES
Spirits:	FULL BAR
Parking:	STREET/PALM GARAGE
Outdoor Dining:	YES

SHAKESPEARE'S ENGLISH PUB

3550 South Osprey Avenue
941-364-5938
shakespearesenglishpub.com

	BRITISH	COST: $$

HOURS: Daily, 11:30AM to 9PM

WHAT TO EXPECT: Great for after work meet-up • Good for lunch
Fantastic burger • Traditional English fare

CARRYOUT/DELIVERY INFO: Full menu available for carryout and
delivery. Curbside pick up. Delivery available through Grubhub,
Bite Squad and DoorDash.

SCAN FOR MENU

SOME BASICS
Reservations:	NO
Spirits:	BEER/WINE
Parking:	LOT
Outdoor Dining:	YES

SHANER'S PIZZA
6500 Superior Avenue
941-927-2708
shanerspizza.com

GULF GATE	PIZZA	COST: $$

HOURS: Sun & Mon, 11:30AM to 9PM • Tue-Sat, 4:30PM to 10PM

WHAT TO EXPECT: Pizza and more • Casual atmosphere
Good place to catch the game

CARRYOUT/DELIVERY INFO: Full menu available for carryout and delivery, Curbside pick up. Delivery available through Bite Squad.

SCAN FOR MENU

SOME BASICS

Reservations:	NO
Spirits:	BEER/WINE
Parking:	LOT/STREET
Outdoor Dining:	YES

SHARKY'S ON THE PIER
1600 Harbor Drive South
941-488-1456
sharkysonthepier.com

VENICE	AMERICAN	COST: $$

HOURS: Sun-Thur, 11:30AM to 10PM • Fri & Sat, 11:30AM to 11PM

WHAT TO EXPECT: Live music • On the beach • Very "Florida"
Voted Florida's Best Beach Bar ('13, '18, '19)

CARRYOUT/DELIVERY INFO: Full menu available for carryout. Curbside and contactless pick up. Delivery not available.

SCAN FOR MENU

SOME BASICS

Reservations:	YES
Spirits:	FULL BAR
Parking:	LOT
Outdoor Dining:	YES

SHORE DINER
465 John Ringling Boulevard*
941-296-0301
dineshore.com

ST. ARMANDS	AMERICAN	COST: $$$

HOURS: Mon-Sat, 12PM to 9PM • Sun, 10AM to 9PM

WHAT TO EXPECT: Online reservations • Busy during season
Good wine list • Happy Hour

CARRYOUT/DELIVERY INFO: Online ordering available. Full menu available for carryout. Curbside and contactless pick up. Delivery not available.

SCAN FOR MENU

SOME BASICS
Reservations:	YES
Spirits:	FULL BAR
Parking:	STREET
Outdoor Dining:	YES

SIEGFRIED'S RESTAURANT
1869 Fruitville Road
941-330-9330
siegfrieds-restaurant.com

DOWNTOWN	GERMAN	COST: $$

HOURS: Wed-Sun, 4PM to 10PM
CLOSED MONDAY & TUESDAY

WHAT TO EXPECT: Casual dining • Family owned
Authentic German cuisine • German beer-garden

CARRYOUT/DELIVERY INFO: Full menu available for carryout. Curbside pick up. Delivery not available.

SCAN FOR MENU

SOME BASICS
Reservations:	YES
Spirits:	BEER/WINE
Parking:	LOT/STREET
Outdoor Dining:	YES

SIESTA KEY OYSTER BAR (SKOB)
5238 Ocean Boulevard
941-346-5443
skob.com

SIESTA KEY	AMERICAN	COST: $$

HOURS: Mon-Thur, 11AM to 12AM • Fri & Sat, 11AM to 2AM
Sun, 9AM to 12AM

WHAT TO EXPECT: Vacation atmosphere • Live music daily
Sunday brunch • Great for families • Busy in season

CARRYOUT/DELIVERY INFO: Most menu items available for
carryout. Curbside pick up. Delivery not available.

SCAN FOR MENU

SOME BASICS

Reservations:	NO
Spirits:	FULL BAR
Parking:	LOT/STREET
Outdoor Dining:	YES

SIMON'S COFFEE HOUSE
5900 South Tamiami Trail
941-926-7151
simonstogo.com

SOUTH TRAIL	DELI	COST: $$

HOURS: Mon-Sat, 8AM to 4PM

WHAT TO EXPECT: Sandwiches • Salads • Vegan & Vegetarian options

CARRYOUT/DELIVERY INFO: Full menu available for carryout
and delivery. Curbside and contactless pick up. Delivery available
through Bite Squad, Uber Eats and DoorDash.

SCAN FOR MENU

SOME BASICS

Reservations:	NO
Spirits:	BEER/WINE
Parking:	LOT
Outdoor Dining:	NO

SMOQEHOUSE

6112 South Tamiami Trail
941-923-9090
smoqehouse.com

SOUTH TRAIL	BBQ	COST: $$

HOURS: Mon-Sat, 11AM to 8PM • CLOSED SUNDAY

WHAT TO EXPECT: BBQ • Great sandwiches • Super casual
Good for a quick lunch

CARRYOUT/DELIVERY INFO: Online ordering available. Full menu available for carryout and delivery. Delivery is available through Bite Squad.

SCAN FOR MENU

SOME BASICS

Reservations:	NO
Spirits:	BEER/WINE
Parking:	LOT
Outdoor Dining:	NO

SNOOK HAVEN

5000 East Venice Avenue
941-485-7221
snookhaven.com

VENICE	AMERICAN	COST: $$

HOURS: Wed-Sun, 11:30AM to 8PM
CLOSED MONDAY & TUESDAY

WHAT TO EXPECT: Old Florida • Super unique setting
Canoe & kayak rentals • Banjo Thursdays!

CARRYOUT/DELIVERY INFO: Full menu available for carryout. Curbside and contactless pick up. Delivery not available.

SCAN FOR MENU

SOME BASICS

Reservations:	NO
Spirits:	BEER/WINE
Parking:	LOT
Outdoor Dining:	YES

SOUTH PHILLY CHEESESTEAKS

1439 Main Street*
941-330-8208
thecheapestwaytophilly.com/mainstreet

DOWNTOWN	AMERICAN	COST: $$

HOURS: Mon-Sat, 10:30AM to 9PM • CLOSED SUNDAY

WHAT TO EXPECT: Cheesesteaks! • Shakes and malts
Great for a quick lunch • Authentic Philly hoagies

CARRYOUT/DELIVERY INFO: Full menu available for carryout and delivery. Delivery available through Bite Squad and Uber Eats.

SCAN FOR MENU

SOME BASICS
Reservations:	NO
Spirits:	BEER/WINE
Parking:	STREET
Outdoor Dining:	NO

SOUTHSIDE DELI

1825 Hillview Street
941-330-9302
southsidedelisarasota.com

SOUTHSIDE VILLAGE	DELI	COST: $$

HOURS: Mon-Fri, 7AM to 8PM • Sat, 7AM to 6PM
CLOSED SUNDAY

WHAT TO EXPECT: Deli sandwiches • Quick service
Great salads • Drive thru service

CARRYOUT/DELIVERY INFO: Full menu available for carryout and delivery. Drive through pick up. Delivery available through Grubhub.

SCAN FOR MENU

SOME BASICS
Reservations:	NO
Spirits:	NONE
Parking:	STREET
Outdoor Dining:	YES

SPEAKS CLAM BAR

29 North Boulevard of Presidents*
941-232-7633
speaksclambar.com

ST. ARMANDS	SEAFOOD	COST: $$$

HOURS: Mon-Wed, 4:30M to 10PM • Thur, 11AM to 10PM
Fri & Sat, 11AM to11PM • Sun, 12PM to 10PM

WHAT TO EXPECT: Clams! • "Italian" clam bar • Online reservations
Gluten free menu • Good for groups

CARRYOUT/DELIVERY INFO: Online ordering available. Full menu
available for carryout and delivery. Curbside and contactless
pick up. Delivery available through Uber Eats and Bite Squad.

SCAN FOR MENU

SOME BASICS

Reservations:	YES
Spirits:	FULL BAR
Parking:	GARAGE/STREET
Outdoor Dining:	YES

SPEARFISH GRILLE

1265 Old Stickney Point Road
941-349-1971
spearfishgrille.com

SIESTA KEY	SEAFOOD	COST: $$

HOURS: Daily, 11AM to 10PM

WHAT TO EXPECT: Super casual • Island feel
Small menu • Good for families

CARRYOUT/DELIVERY INFO: Full menu available for carryout.
Delivery not available.

SCAN FOR MENU

SOME BASICS

Reservations:	NONE
Spirits:	FULL BAR
Parking:	LOT/STREET
Outdoor Dining:	YES

SPICE STATION

1438 Boulevard of the Arts
941-343-2894
spicestationsrq.com

DOWNTOWN	THAI/SUSHI	COST: $$

HOURS: Mon-Thur, 11AM to 9PM • Fri, 11AM to 9:30PM
Sat 12PM to 9:30PM • CLOSED SUNDAY

WHAT TO EXPECT: Casual Asian cuisine • Quaint and comfortable
Vegetarian options • Thai and sushi

CARRYOUT/DELIVERY INFO: Full menu available for carryout and delivery. Curbside pick up. Delivery available through Bite Squad, Uber Eats and DoorDash.

SCAN FOR MENU

SOME BASICS
Reservations:	YES
Spirits:	BEER/WINE
Parking:	LOT/STREET
Outdoor Dining:	YES

STAR THAI AND SUSHI

240 Avenida Madera*
941-217-6758
starthaisushisiestakey.com

SIESTA KEY	ASIAN	COST: $$

HOURS: Wed-Mon, 12PM to 11PM • CLOSED TUESDAY

WHAT TO EXPECT: Sushi • Siesta Village • Very friendly staff
Live music

CARRYOUT/DELIVERY INFO: Full menu available for carryout and delivery. Delivery through Bite Squad, Uber Eats and DoorDash.

SCAN FOR MENU

SOME BASICS
Reservations:	YES
Spirits:	FULL BAR
Parking:	STREET/LOT
Outdoor Dining:	YES

STATE STREET EATING HOUSE

1533 State Street
941-951-1533
statestreetsrq.com

DOWNTOWN	AMERICAN	COST: $$

HOURS: Lunch: Tues-Sat, 11:30AM to 2PM
Dinner: Tues-Sat, 5:30PM to 9:30PM

WHAT TO EXPECT: Great for a date • Comfort food • Good wine list
Sat. & Sun. brunch

CARRYOUT/DELIVERY INFO: Online ordering available. Full menu available for carryout and delivery. Curbside pick up. Delivery available through Bite Squad.

SCAN FOR MENU

SOME BASICS

Reservations:	5 OR MORE
Spirits:	FULL BAR
Parking:	LOT
Outdoor Dining:	YES

STATION 400

400 Lemon Avenue*
941-906-1400
station400.com

ROSEMARY DISTRICT	AMERICAN	COST: $$

HOURS: Daily, 7:30AM to 2:30PM

WHAT TO EXPECT: Great for lunch meet-up • Lots of pancakes
Soups, salads, & sandwiches • Catering

CARRYOUT/DELIVERY INFO: Full menu available for carryout. Delivery not available.

SCAN FOR MENU

SOME BASICS

Reservations:	NO
Spirits:	BEER/WINE
Parking:	LOT
Outdoor Dining:	YES

STIKS

4413 South Tamiami Trail
941-923-2742
stiksfoods.com

SOUTH TRAIL	ASIAN	COST: $$

HOURS: Tue-Thur, 11:30AM to 8PM • Fri & Sat, 11:30AM to 8:30PM
Sun, 11:30AM to 8PM • CLOSED MONDAY

WHAT TO EXPECT: Fast casual Asian cuisine • Boba!
Lots of vegan options • Great for a quick lunch

CARRYOUT/DELIVERY INFO: Full menu available for carryout.
Delivery coming spring of 2022.

SCAN FOR MENU

SOME BASICS
Reservations:	NO
Spirits:	FULL BAR
Parking:	LOT
Outdoor Dining:	NO

STOTTLEMEYER'S SMOKEHOUSE

19 East Road
941-312-5969
stottlemyerssmokehouse.com

	BBQ	COST: $$

HOURS: Mon-Wed, 11:30AM to 8PM • Thur, 11:30AM to 9PM
Fri & Sat, 11:30PM to 10PM • Sun, 11:30AM to 9PM

WHAT TO EXPECT: Good for families • Easy on the wallet
Live music • Casual Florida dining experience

CARRYOUT/DELIVERY INFO: Online ordering available. Full menu
available for carryout and delivery. Curbside pick up. Delivery
available through Chow Now.

SCAN FOR MENU

SOME BASICS
Reservations:	YES
Spirits:	FULL BAR
Parking:	LOT
Outdoor Dining:	YES

SUMMER HOUSE STEAK & SEAFOOD

149 Avenida Messina
941-260-2675
summerhousesiestakey.com

SIESTA KEY	STEAKHOUSE	COST: $$$

HOURS: Sun-Thur, 4PM to 10PM
Fri & Sat, 4PM to 11PM

WHAT TO EXPECT: Bustling atmosphere • Happy Hour
Convenient Siesta Key location • Excellent wine list

CARRYOUT/DELIVERY INFO: Full menu available for carryout.
Curbside pick up available by special request only.
Delivery not available.

SCAN FOR MENU

SOME BASICS
Reservations:	YES
Spirits:	FULL BAR
Parking:	STREET/VALET
Outdoor Dining:	YES

SUN GARDEN CAFÉ

210 Avenida Madera
941-346-7170
sungardencafe.com

SIESTA KEY	AMERICAN	COST: $$

HOURS: Daily, 7:30AM to 1:30PM

WHAT TO EXPECT: Casual island lunch • Nice outdoor seating
Sandwich/soup/salad combos

CARRYOUT/DELIVERY INFO: Full menu available for carryout.
Curbside pick up. Delivery not available.

SCAN FOR MENU

SOME BASICS
Reservations:	NO
Spirits:	BEER/WINE
Parking:	STREET
Outdoor Dining:	YES

SUNNYSIDE CAFE
4900 North Tamiami Trail
941-359-9500
sunnysidecafesrq.com

NORTH TRAIL	AMERICAN	COST: $$

HOURS: Lunch, Mon-Fri 9AM to 3PM • Sat, 8AM to 3PM
Dinner, Tues-Sat, 5PM to 9PM • CLOSED SUNDAY

WHAT TO EXPECT: Small, very casual • Family owned and operated
Sandwich/soup/salad combos • Online reservations

CARRYOUT/DELIVERY INFO: Full menu available for carryout.
Delivery available through Bite Squad and Door Dash.

SCAN FOR MENU

SOME BASICS
Reservations:	YES
Spirits:	BEER/WINE
Parking:	LOT
Outdoor Dining:	YES

TASTE OF HONG KONG
2224 Gulf Gate Drive
941-922-6765
tasteofhongkong.net

GULF GATE	CHINESE	COST: $$

HOURS: Mon-Sat, 11:30AM to 10PM
Sun, 4:30PM to 9PM

WHAT TO EXPECT: Chinese carryout • Casual atmosphere
Try the Crispy Duck • Online ordering

CARRYOUT/DELIVERY INFO: Full menu available for carryout.
Delivery not available.

SCAN FOR MENU

SOME BASICS
Reservations:	YES
Spirits:	BEER/WINE
Parking:	LOT
Outdoor Dining:	NO

TASTY HOME COOKIN'

3854 South Tuttle Avenue
941-921-4969
tastyhomecookinsarasota.com

TUTTLE BEE PLAZA	AMERICAN	COST: $

HOURS: Mon-Fri, 7AM to 6PM • Sat, 7AM to 2PM
Sun, 8AM to 2PM

WHAT TO EXPECT: Great for families • Easy on the wallet
Comfort food • Casual dining • Good for kids

CARRYOUT/DELIVERY INFO: Full menu available for carryout and delivery. Delivery available through Bite Squad.

SOME BASICS

SCAN FOR MENU

Reservations: NO
Spirits: BEER/WINE
Parking: LOT
Outdoor Dining: NO

EXPERIENCE A SARASOTA FOOD TOUR

KEY CULINARY TOURS

WHAT TO EXPECT: Culinary walking tours of neighborhoods in Sarasota, St. Armands, Anna Maria island and Venice. Lunch and dinner tours. A great opportunity to sample local foods; meet restaurateurs, discover sarasota neighborhoods and meet new friends! They're Sarasota's original culinary touring company.
MORE INFO: keyculinarytours.com or 941-893-4664

TASTE MAGAZINE PROGRESSIVE DINNERS

WHAT TO EXPECT: Remember the neighborhood progressive dinner? This your chance to experience an upgraded version of the classic food adventure. Taste Magazine sponsors themed progressive dinners about once every six weeks starting December 11th. Their walking historical and food tour of Bradenton departs every Wednesday & Thursday at 12PM. That's a fun way to spend a Florida afternoon.
MORE INFO: tasteweb.net or 941-366-7950

TOASTED MANGO CAFÉ

430 North Tamiami Trail*
941-388-7728
toastedmangocafe.com

NORTH TRAIL	AMERICAN	COST: $$

HOURS: Daily, 7AM to 3PM

WHAT TO EXPECT: Good for families • Casual dining • Great service
Lots of menu choices

CARRYOUT/DELIVERY INFO: Full menu available for carryout.
Curbside pick up. Limited delivery available. Call the restaurant to
order and for delivery details.

SCAN FOR MENU

SOME BASICS

Reservations:	NO
Spirits:	FULL BAR
Parking:	LOT
Outdoor Dining:	NO

TOMMY BAHAMA CAFÉ

300 John Ringling Boulevard
941-388-2888
tommybahama.com

ST. ARMANDS	AMERICAN	COST: $$

HOURS: Sun-Thur, 11AM to 8:30PM • Fri & Sat, 11AM to 9:30PM

WHAT TO EXPECT: Great for a relaxing lunch • Island time Happy Hour
St. Armands Circle • OpenTable reservations

CARRYOUT/DELIVERY INFO: Online ordering. Full menu available
for carryout and delivery. Curbside and contactless pick up.
Delivery available through Chow Now.

SCAN FOR MENU

SOME BASICS

Reservations:	YES
Spirits:	FULL BAR
Parking:	STREET
Outdoor Dining:	YES

TONY'S CHICAGO BEEF

6569 Superior Avenue*
941-922-7979
tonyschicagobeef.com

GULF GATE	AMERICAN	COST: $

HOURS: Mon-Sat, 11AM to 9PM
CLOSED SUNDAY

WHAT TO EXPECT: Great for lunch • Easy on the wallet
Chicago style food • Counter and table seating

CARRYOUT/DELIVERY INFO: Full menu available for carryout and delivery. Delivery available through Bite Squad.

SCAN FOR MENU

SOME BASICS

Reservations:	NO
Spirits:	BEER/WINE
Parking:	LOT/STREET
Outdoor Dining:	YES

TRIPLETAIL SEAFOOD & SPIRITS   `NEW`

4870 South Tamiami Trail
941-529-0555
tripletailsrq.com

THE LANDINGS	SEAFOOD	COST: $$$

HOURS: Sun-Thur, 3PM to 9PM
Fri & Sat, 3PM to 10PM

WHAT TO EXPECT: Upscale, casual seafood • OpenTable reservations
Busy in season • Handcrafted cocktails

CARRYOUT/DELIVERY INFO: Full menu available for carryout.
Delivery not available.

SCAN FOR MENU

SOME BASICS

Reservations:	YES
Spirits:	FULL BAR
Parking:	LOT
Outdoor Dining:	YES

TURTLES ON LITTLE SARASOTA BAY

8875 Midnight Pass Road
941-346-2207
turtlesrestaurant.com

SIESTA KEY	AMERICAN	COST: $$

HOURS: Daily, 11:30AM to 9PM

WHAT TO EXPECT: Right on the water • Old style Florida dining
Sunday brunch • Happy Hour specials

CARRYOUT/DELIVERY INFO: Special carryout menu. Curbside and contactless pick up. Delivery not available.

SCAN FOR MENU

SOME BASICS
Reservations:	YES
Spirits:	FULL BAR
Parking:	LOT
Outdoor Dining:	YES

VEG

6538 Gateway Avenue
941-312-6424
vegsrq.com

GULF GATE	VEGETARIAN	COST: $$

HOURS: Lunch, Mon-Sat, 11AM to 2PM
Dinner, Mon-Sat, 5PM to 8PM • CLOSED SUNDAY

WHAT TO EXPECT: Vegan/Veg • Daily specials
One of Sarasota's oldest vegetarian restaurants

CARRYOUT/DELIVERY INFO: Online ordering. Full menu available for carryout and delivery. Curbside pick up. Delivery through Bite Squad and Uber Eats.

SCAN FOR MENU

SOME BASICS
Reservations:	YES
Spirits:	BEER/WINE
Parking:	LOT/STREET
Outdoor Dining:	NO

VERONICA FISH & OYSTER

1830 South Osprey Avenue
941-366-1342
veronicafishandoyster.com

SOUTHSIDE VILLAGE	SEAFOOD	COST: $$$

HOURS: Tue-Thur, 5PM to 9PM • Fri & Sat, 5PM to 10PM
CLOSED SUNDAY & MONDAY

WHAT TO EXPECT: Busy, lively dining room • Handmade cocktails
Raw bar • Upscale dining

CARRYOUT/DELIVERY INFO: ** *At press time, we were not able
to verify the carryout and delivery options for this restaurant. We
suggest you call for their most up to date information.* **

SOME BASICS

Reservations:	YES
Spirits:	FULL BAR
Parking:	LOT/STREET
Outdoor Dining:	YES

SCAN FOR MENU

ABOUT US

Way back in April 2002 we started dineSarasota as a way to bring up to date restaurant and dining information to Sarasota locals and visitors. Our annual printed dining guides and our website, dineSarasota.com, have grown right along with the ever expanding Sarasota dining scene. Whether you're just visiting or you're a native, we're here to help you make the most of your local dining experiences.

VILLAGE CAFÉ

5133 Ocean Boulevard
941-349-2822
villagecafeonsiesta.com

SIESTA KEY	AMERICAN	COST: $$

HOURS: Daily, 7AM to 2:30PM

WHAT TO EXPECT: Family owned • Dog friendly outdoor dining
Casual dining • Heart of Siesta Village • Good for familes

CARRYOUT/DELIVERY INFO: Full menu available for carryout and
delivery. Curbside pick up. Delivery available through Bite Squad
and Uber Eats.

SCAN FOR MENU

SOME BASICS
Reservations:	NO
Spirits:	BEER/WINE
Parking:	STREET
Outdoor Dining:	YES

WALT'S FISH MARKET

4144 South Tamiami Trail
941-921-4605
waltsfishmarketrestaurant.com

SOUTH TRAIL	SEAFOOD	COST: $$

HOURS: Daily, 11AM to 9PM • Market, 9AM to 8PM
Chickee Bar, 11AM to 11PM

WHAT TO EXPECT: Restaurant & market • Live music • Casual dining
Busy in season • Since 1918!

CARRYOUT/DELIVERY INFO: Full menu available for carryout.
Curbside pick up. Delivery not available.

SCAN FOR MENU

SOME BASICS
Reservations:	NO
Spirits:	FULL BAR
Parking:	LOT
Outdoor Dining:	YES

THE WHISKEY BARREL

NEW

15 South Boulevard of the Presidents
941-529-0555
thewhiskeybarrelbar.com

ST. ARMANDS	AMERICAN	COST: $$

HOURS: Tue-Thur, 2PM to 11PM • Fri, 2PM to 1AM
Sat, 11AM to 1AM • Sun, 11AM to 10PM • CLOSED MONDAY

WHAT TO EXPECT: Great whiskey selection • Live music
Event space • Sandwiches & pizza

CARRYOUT/DELIVERY INFO: Full menu available for carryout and delivery, Delivery available through Grubhub.

SCAN FOR MENU

SOME BASICS
Reservations:	NO
Spirits:	FULL BAR
Parking:	STREET/GARAGE
Outdoor Dining:	YES

WICKED CANTINA

1603 North Tamiami Trail*
941-706-2395
wickedcantina.com

NORTH TRAIL	TEX MEX	COST: $$

HOURS: Daily, 11AM to 10PM

WHAT TO EXPECT: Casual dining • Convenient before a show
Busy in season • Happy Hour daily

CARRYOUT/DELIVERY INFO: Online ordering. Full menu available for carryout. Curbside pick up. No delivery available.

SCAN FOR MENU

SOME BASICS
Reservations:	YES
Spirits:	FULL BAR
Parking:	LOT
Outdoor Dining:	NO

LOCAL FARMERS MARKET INFORMATION

SARASOTA FARMERS MARKET
Lemon Avenue
Downtown Sarasota
Saturdays (Year Round)
7AM to 1PM
Rain or Shine
70+ Vendors
sarasotafarmersmarket.org

DOWNTOWN BRADENTON PUBLIC MARKET
Old Main Street (12 St. W)
Saturdays (October thru May)
9AM to 2PM
realizebradenton.com/about-the-market

SIESTA KEY FARMERS MARKET
Davidson's Plaza (5104 Ocean Boulevard)
Sundays (Year Round)
8AM to 12PM
Rain or Shine
siestakeyfarmersmarket.org

PHILLIPPI FARMHOUSE MARKET
Phillippi Estates Park (5500 South Tamiami Trail)
Wednesdays (October thru April)
9AM to 2PM
50+ Vendors
farmhousemarket.org

WHAT'S IN SEASON?

Our Sarasota area farmer's markets really give locals and visitors a taste of fresh Florida flavor. But, our markets are more than a place just to stock up for the week. They're a place to mingle with friends, enjoy some music or catch up on the latest neighborhood news!

Now you have good list of places to buy the freshest locally grown produce. But, what's the best time of year to enjoy Florida's fruits and vegetables? When are they at their peak of freshness? Here's a little help.

WINTER > Bell Pepper • Eggplant • Grapefruit
Strawberries • Squash • Tomatoes • Arugula • Kale
SPRING > Cantaloupe • Guava • Lettuce • Mushrooms
Oranges • Papaya • Radish • Swiss Chard • Strawberries
SUMMER > Avocado • Guava • Mango • Eggplant
Peanuts • Sweet Corn • Watermelon • Snow Peas
FALL > Cucumber • Grapefruit • Mushrooms • Lettuce
Snap Beans • Tangerines • Tomatoes • Peppers

We have super fresh seafood here in Sarasota. You can usually find a plentiful supply of grouper, red snapper, pompano, and mahi at our farmers markets. Of course, you can always find fresh Gulf shrimp in a variety of sizes.

The most anticipated seafood season runs from October 15th through May 1st. That's stone crab season! You're best off to grab these tasty delights towards the beginning of season when they're the most plentiful.

WORD OF MOUTH

6604 Gateway Avenue
941-925-2400
originalwordofmouth.com

GULF GATE	AMERICAN	COST: $$

HOURS: Daily, 8AM to 2PM

WHAT TO EXPECT: Daily specials • Casual dining • Good for families

CARRYOUT/DELIVERY INFO: Online ordering. Full menu available for carryout. Curbside and contactless pick up.
Delivery not available.

SCAN FOR MENU

SOME BASICS
Reservations:	NO
Spirits:	BEER/WINE
Parking:	LOT/STREET
Outdoor Dining:	NO

YODER'S RESTAURANT

3434 Bahia Vista Street
941-955-7771
yodersrestaurant.com

PINECRAFT	AMISH	COST: $

HOURS: Mon-Sat, 7AM to 8PM • CLOSED SUNDAY

WHAT TO EXPECT: Great for families • Easy on the wallet
Busy in season • Fantastic service • Pie!!

CARRYOUT/DELIVERY INFO: Online ordering. Full menu available for carryout and delivery. Delivery through Bite Squad.

SCAN FOR MENU

SOME BASICS
Reservations:	NO
Spirits:	NONE
Parking:	LOT
Outdoor Dining:	NO

YUME SUSHI

1532 Main Street
941-363-0604
yumerestaurant.com

DOWNTOWN	SUSHI	COST: $$

HOURS: Lunch, Mon-Sat, 11:30AM to 2PM
Dinner, Mon-Sun, 5PM to Close

WHAT TO EXPECT: Great for a date • Fun dining experience
Great sake selection

CARRYOUT/DELIVERY INFO: Full menu available for carryout and delivery. Curbside pick up. Delivery available through Bite Squad.

SCAN FOR MENU

SOME BASICS

Reservations:	6 OR MORE
Spirits:	BEER/WINE
Parking:	STREET
Outdoor Dining:	NO

YUMMY HOUSE

1737 South Tamiami Trail
941-351-1688
yummyhouseflorida.com

SOUTH TRAIL	ASIAN	COST: $$

HOURS: Lunch, Daily, 11AM to 2:30PM • Dim Sum, 11AM to 2:30PM
Dinner, Mon-Sat, 5PM to 9:30PM • Sun, 5PM to 9PM

WHAT TO EXPECT: Busy in season • Lively atmosphere
Lots of parking

CARRYOUT/DELIVERY INFO: Online ordering. Full menu available for carryout and delivery. Delivery through DoorDash.

SCAN FOR MENU

SOME BASICS

Reservations:	YES
Spirits:	FULL BAR
Parking:	LOT
Outdoor Dining:	NO

Restaurant Name	Address	Phone #
A Sprig of Thyme	1962 Hillview St	330-8890
Almazonica Cerveceria	4141 S Tamiami Trl	260-5964
Amore	180 N Lime Ave	383-1111
Andrea's	2085 Siesta Dr	951-9200
Anna Maria Oyster Bar	6696 Cortez Rd	792-0077
Anna Maria Oyster Bar	1525 51st Ave E	721-7773
Anna's Deli	6535 Midnight Pass	348-4888
Apollonia Grill	8235 Cooper Creek	359-4816
Athen's Family Rest.	2300 Bee Ridge Rd	706-4121
Atmosphere	935 N Beneva Rd	203-8542
Baker & Wife	2157 Siesta Dr	960-1765
Bavaro's Pizza	27 Fletcher Ave	552-9131
Beach Bistro	6600 Gulf Dr N	778-6444
Beach House Restaurant	200 Gulf Dr N	779-2222
Bevardi's Salute!	23 N Lemon Ave	365-1020
Big Water Fish Market	6641 Midgnight Pass	554-8101
Bijou Café	1287 First St	366-8111
Blu Kouzina	25 N Blvd of Pres	388-2619
Blue Rooster	1524 Fourth St	388-5739
Boca Kitchen, Bar, Mkt	21 S Lemon Ave	256-3565
The Bodhi Tree	1938 Adams Ln	702-8552
Bohemios Tapas Bar	3246 Clark Rd	260-9784
Bonjour French Cafe	5214 Ocean Blvd	346-0600
Breakfast at Victoria's	4141 S Tamiami Trl	923-6441
The Breakfast House	1817 Fruitville Rd	366-6860
Brine Seafood	2250 Gulf Gate Dr	404-5639
Brick's Smoked Meats	1528 State St	993-1435

Restaurant Name	Address	Phone #
Bushido Izayaki	3688 Webber St	217-5635
Buttermilk Handcrafted	5520 Palmer Blvd	487-8949
Café Baci	4001 S Tamiami Trl	921-4848
Café Barbosso	5501 Palmer Crossing	922-7999
Café Epicure	1298 Main St	366-5648
Café Gabbiano	5104 Ocean Blvd	349-1423
Cafe in the Park	2010 Adams Ln	361-3032
Café L'Europe	431 St Armands Cir	388-4415
Café Longet	239 Miami Ave W	244-2643
Capt. Brian's Seafood	8421 N Tamiami Trl	351-4492
Capt. Curt's Oyster Bar	1200 Old Stickney Pt	349-3885
Caragiulos	69 S Palm Ave	951-0866
Casey Key Fish House	801 Blackburn Pt Rd	966-1901
Cask & Ale	1548 Main St	702-8740
Cassariano Italian Eat.	313 W Venice Ave	485-0507
C'est La Vie!	1553 Main St	906-9575
Cha Cha Coconuts	417 St Armands Cir	388-3300
Circo	1435 2nd St	253-0978
Clasico Italian Chophse	1341 Main St	957-0700
Clayton's Siesta Grille	1256 Old Stickney Pt	349-2800
The Columbia	411 St Armands Cir	388-3987
Connors Steakhouse	3501 S Tamiami Trl	260-3232
The Cottage	153 Avenida Messina	312-9300
Crab & Fin	420 St Armands Cir	388-3964
The Crow's Nest	1968 Tarpon Ctr Dr	484-9551
Curry Station	3550 Clark Rd	924-7222
Daiquiri Deck Raw Bar	5250 Ocean Blvd	349-8697

Restaurant Name	Address	Phone #
Daiquiri Deck Raw Bar	325 John Ringling Blvd	388-3325
Daiquiri Deck Raw Bar	300 W Venice Ave	488-0649
Daiquiri Deck Raw Bar	1250 Stickney Pt Rd	312-2422
DaRuMa Japanese	5459 Fruitville Rd	342-6600
DaRuMa Japanese	4910 S. Tamiami Trl	552-9465
Der Dutchman	3713 Bahia Vista	955-8007
Dim Sum King	8194 Tourist Center Dr	306-5848
Dix Coney Cafe	6525 Superior Ave	927-1672
Doggystyle	1544 Main St	260-5835
Dolce Italia	6606 Superior Ave	921-7007
Drift Kitchen	700 Benjamin Franklin	388-2161
Drunken Poet Café	1572 Main St	955-8404
Dry Dock Waterfront	412 Gulf of Mexico Dr	383-0102
Dutch Valley Restaurant	6731 S Tamiami Trl	924-1770
Duval's, Fresh, Local...	1435 Main St	312-4001
El Melvin Cocina	1355 Main St	366-1618
El Toro Bravo	3218 Clark Rd	924-0006
Element	1413 Main St	724-8585
Euphemia Haye	5540 Gulf of Mexico Dr	383-3633
EVOQ	1175 N. Gulfstream	260-8255
1592 Wood Fired Kitch	1592 Main St	365-2234
Figaro Bistro	1944 Hillview St	960-2109
Fins At Sharky's	1600 Harbor Dr S	999-3467
Flavio's Brick Oven	5239 Ocean Blvd	349-0995
Gecko's Grill & Pub	6606 S Tamiami Trl	248-2020
Gecko's Grill & Pub	5588 Palmer Crossing	923-6061
Gecko's Grill & Pub	351 N Cattlemen Rd	378-0077
Gecko's Grill & Pub	1900 Hillview St	953-2929

Restaurant Name	Address	Phone #
Gentile Cheesesteaks	7523 S Tamiami Trl	926-0441
Gilligan's Island Bar	5253 Ocean Blvd	349-4759
The Grasshopper	7253 S Tamiami Trl	923-3688
Grillsmith's	6240 S Tamiami Trl	259-8383
GROVE Restaurant	10670 Boardwalk Lp	893-4321
Gulf Gate Food & Beer	6528 Superior Ave	952-3361
Harry's Continental Kit.	525 St Judes Dr	383-0777
Hob Nob Drive-In	1701 Washington Blvd	955-5001
Hoshi Sushi	6516 Superior Ave	923-8888
The Hub Baha Grill	5148 Ocean Blvd	349-6800
Il Panificio	1703 Main St	366-5570
Il Panificio	215 Avenida Madera	800-5570
Indigenous	239 Links Ave	706-4740
Inkawasi Peruvian	10667 Boardwalk Lp	360-1110
Irish 31	3750 S Tamiami Trl	234-9265
Island House Tap & Grl.	5110 Ocean Blvd	312-9205
Island House Taqueria	2773 Bee Ridge Rd	922-8226
Jack Dusty	1111 Ritz-Carlton Dr	309-2266
Joey D's Chicago Style	3811 Kenny Dr.	378-8900
Joey D's Chicago Style	211 N Tamiami Trl	364-9900
Jpan Sushi & Grill	3 Paradise Plaza	954-5726
Jpan Sushi & Grill	229 N Cattlemen Rd	954-5726
JR's Old Packinghouse	987 S Packinghse Rd	371-9358
Ka Papa Vegan	1830 S Osprey Ave	600-8590
Karl Ehmer's Alpine	4520 S Tamiami Trl	922-3797
Kiyoski's Sushi	6550 Gateway Ave	924-3781
Knick's Tavern & Grill	1818 S Osprey Ave	955-7761
Kojo	1289 N Palm Ave	536-9717

Restaurant Name	Address	Phone #
Korean Ssam Bar	1303 N Washington	312-6264
L&L Hawaiian Barbecue	5445 Fruitville Rd	315-9008
La Norma	5370 Gulf of Mexico Dr	383-6262
Lazy Lobster	5350 Gulf of Mexico Dr	388-0440
Lazy Lobster	7602 N Lockwood Rg	351-5515
Libby's Brasserie	1917 S Osprey Ave	487-7300
Lila	1576 Main St	296-1042
The Lily Cafe	4832 S Tamiami Trl	554-8700
Little Saigon Bistro	2725 S Beneva Rd	312-4730
The Lobster Pot	5157 Ocean Blvd	349-2323
Lovely Square	6559 Gateway Ave	724-2512
Made	1990 Main St	953-2900
Mademoiselle Paris	8527 Cooper Creek Bl	355-2323
Mademoiselle Paris	1605 Main St	544-4021
Madfish Grill	4059 Cattlemen Rd	377-3474
Main Bar Sandwich Shp	1944 Main St	955-8733
Maison Blanche	2605 Gulf of Mexico Dr	383-8088
Mandeville Beer Garden	428 N Lemon Ave	954-8688
Mar-Vista Restaurant	760 Broadway St	383-2391
Marcello's Ristorante	4155 S Tamiami Trl	921-6794
Marina Jack's	2 Marina Plaza	365-4243
Mattison's City Grille	1 N Lemon Ave	330-0440
Mattison's Forty One	7275 S Tamiami Trl	921-3400
Mediterraneo	1970 Main St	365-4122
Melange	1568 Main St	953-7111
Michael John's	1040 Carlton Arms	747-8032
Michael's On East	1212 East Ave	366-0007

Restaurant Name	Address	Phone #
Michelle's Brown Bag	1819 Main St	365-5858
Miguel's	6631 Midnight Pass	349-4024
Millie's Cafe	3900 Clark Rd	923-4054
Monk's Steamer Bar	6690 Superior Ave	927-3388
Munchies 420 Café	6639 Superior Ave	929-9893
99 Bottles Taproom	1445 2nd St	487-7874
Nancy's Bar-B-Que	14475 SR 70	999-2390
Napule Ristorante	7129 S Tamiami Trl	556-9639
Nellie's Deli	15 S Beneva Rd	924-2705
New Pass Grill	1505 Ken Thompson	388-3050
Nicky's Bistro	49 S Palm Ave	330-1727
Oak & Stone	5405 University Pkwy	225-4590
Oak & Stone	4067 Clark Rd	893-4881
Oasis Café	3542 S Osprey Ave	957-1214
The Old Salty Dog	5023 Ocean Blvd	349-0158
The Old Salty Dog	160 Ken Thompson Pk	388-4311
The Old Salty Dog	1485 S Tamiami Trl	483-1000
O'Leary's Tiki Bar	5 Bayfront Dr	953-7505
Ophelia's on the Bay	9105 Midnight Pass	349-2212
Origin Beer & Pizza	3837 Hillview St	316-9222
Origin Beer & Pizza	5070 Clark Rd	217-6533
Origin Beer & Pizza	8193 Tourist Ctr Dr	358-5850
The Overton	1420 Blvd of the Arts	500-9175
Owen's Fish Camp	516 Burns Ct	951-6936
Pacific Rim	1859 Hillview St	330-8071
Parrot Patio Bar & Grill	3602 Webber St	952-3352
Parrot X-Press	2407 Bee Ridge Rd	922-4000
Pastry Art Bakery	1512 Main St	955-7545

Restaurant Name	Address	Phone #
Patrick's 1481	1481 Main St	955-1481
Pazzo Southside	1936 Hillview St	260-8831
Phillippi Creek Oyster	5363 S Tamiami Trl	925-4444
Pho Cali	1578 Main St	955-2683
Piccolo Italian Market	6518 Gateway Ave	923-2202
Pier 22	1200 1st Avenue W	748-8087
Pizza N' Brew	1507 Main St	359-3894
Pizza N' Brew	6645 Midnight Pass	349-4490
The Point	135 Bayview Dr	218-6114
Poppo's Taqueria	4990 S Tamiami Trl	343-2341
Pop's Sunset Grill	112 Circuit Rd	488-3177
Pub 32	8383 S Tamiami Trl	952-3070
The Public House	6240 N Lockwood Rg	822-0795
Rasoi Indian Kitchen	7119 S Tamiami Trl	921-9200
Reef Cakes	1812 S Osprey Ave	444-7968
Rendez-Vous Bakery	5336 Clark Rd	924-1234
Reyna's Taqueria	935 N Beneva Rd	260-8343
Ripfire Pizza & BBQ	5218 Ocean Blvd	313-7511
Rico's Pizza - Bay Rd	1902 Bay Rd	366-8988
Roessler's	2033 Vamo Way	966-5688
RomanSQ Pizza	6670 Superior Ave	237-8742
Rosebud's Steakhouse	2215 S Tamiami Trl	918-8771
The Rosemary	411 N Orange Ave	955-7600
Rosemary & Thyme	511 N Orange Ave	955-7600
Sage	1216 1st St	445-5660
The Sandbar	100 Spring Ave	778-0444
Sarasota Brewing Comp	6607 Gateway Ave	925-2337
Sardinia	5770 S Tamiami Trl	702-8582

Restaurant Name	Address	Phone #
Schnitzel Kitchen	6521 Superior Ave	922-9299
Screaming Goat Taq.	6606 Superior Ave	210-3992
Selva Grill	1345 Main St	362-4427
Shakespeare's Eng. Pub	3550 S Osprey Ave	364-5938
Shaner's Pizza	6500 Superior Ave	927-2708
Sharky's on the Pier	1600 Harbor Dr S	488-1456
Shore Diner	465 John Ringling	296-0303
Siegfried's Restaurant	1869 Fruitville Rd	330-9330
Siesta Key Oyster Bar	5238 Ocean Blvd	346-5443
Simon's Coffee House	5900 S Tamiami Trl	926-7151
Smoqehouse	6112 S Tamiami Trl	923-9090
Snook Haven	500 E Venice Ave	485-7221
S Philly Cheesesteaks	1439 Main St	330-8208
Southside Deli	1825 Hillview St	330-9302
Speaks Clam Bar	29 N Blvd of Pres.	232-7633
Spear Fish Grille	1265 Old Stickney Pt	349-1970
Spice Station	1438 Blvd of the Arts	343-2894
Star Thai & Sushi	935 N Beneva Rd	706-3848
Star Thai & Sushi	240 Avenida Madera	217-6758
State St. Eating House	1533 State St	951-1533
Station 400	400 Lemon Ave	906-1400
Station 400	8215 Lakewood Main	907-0648
Stiks	4413 S Tamiami Trl	923-2742
Stottlemeyer's Smokehs	19 East Rd	312-5969
Summer House	149 Avenida Messina	206-2675
Sun Garden Café	210 Avenida Madera	346-7170
Sunnyside Cafe	4900 N Tamiami Trl	359-9500

Restaurant Name	Address	Phone #
Taste of Hong Kong	2224 Gulf Gate Dr	922-6765
Tandoor	8453 Cooper Creek	926-3070
Tasty Home Cookin'	3854 S Tuttle Ave	921-4969
Toasted Mango Café	430 N Tamiami Trl	388-7728
Toasted Mango Café	6621 Midnight Pass	552-6485
Tommy Bahama Café	300 John Ringling Blvd	388-2888
Tony's Chicago Beef	6569 Superior Ave	922-7979
Tony's Chicago Beef	1856 S Tamiami - Ven.	497-1611
Tripletail Seafood	4870 S Tamiami Trl	529-0555
Turtle's	8875 Midnight Pass	346-2207
Veg	2164 Gulf Gate Dr	312-6424
Veronica Fish & Oyster	1830 S Osprey Ave	366-1342
Village Café	5133 Ocean Blvd	349-2822
Walt's Fish Market	4144 S Tamiami Trl	921-4605
The Whiskey Barrel	15 S Blvd of Pres.	266-9650
Wicked Cantina	1603 N Tamiami Trl	821-2990
Word of Mouth	6604 Gateway Ave	925-2400
Yoder's Restaurant	3434 Bahia Vista	955-7771
Yume Sushi	1532 Main St	363-0604
Yummy House	1737 S Tamiami Trl	351-1688

Scan for the latest
Sarasota Restaurant
news. Subscribe to
our newsletter
sarasota
bites
on Bulletin

AMERICAN		
Restaurant Name	**Address**	**Phone #**
Baker & Wife	2157 Siesta Dr	960-1765
Beach Bistro	6600 Gulf Dr N	778-6444
Beach House Rest.	200 Gulf Dr N	779-2222
Bijou Café	1287 First St	366-8111
Blue Rooster	1524 Fourth St	388-5739
Boca Kitchen, Bar, Mkt.	21 S. Lemon Ave	256-3565
Breakfast at Victoria's	4141 S Tamiami Trl	923-6441
The Breakfast House	1817 Fruitville Rd	366-6860
Brick's Smoked Meats	1528 State St	993-1435
Buttermilk Handcrafted	5520 Palmer Blvd	487-8949
Cask & Ale	1548 Main St	702-8740
Cha Cha Coconuts	417 St Armands Cir	388-3300
Clayton's Siesta Grille	1256 Old Stickney Pt	349-2800
The Cottage	153 Avenida Messina	312-9300
Daiquiri Deck Raw Bar	5250 Ocean Blvd	349-8697
Daiquiri Deck Raw Bar	325 John Ringling Blvd	388-3325
Daiquiri Deck Raw Bar	300 W Venice Ave	488-0649
Daiquiri Deck Raw Bar	1250 Stickney Pt Rd	312-2422
Dix Coney Cafe	6525 Superior Ave	927-1672
Doggystyle	1544 Main St	260-5835
Drift Kitchen	700 Benjamin Franklin	388-2161
Der Dutchman	3713 Bahia Vista	955-8007
Dutch Valley Restaurant	6731 S Tamiami Trl	924-1770
Duval's, Fresh, Local...	1435 Main St	312-4001
Euphemia Haye	5540 Gulf of Mexico Dr	383-3633
EVOQ	1175 N. Gulfstream	260-8255
Gecko's Grill & Pub	6606 S Tamiami Trl	248-2020

AMERICAN		
Restaurant Name	Address	Phone #
Gecko's Grill & Pub	1900 Hillview St	953-2929
Gecko's Grill & Pub	5588 Palmer Crossing	923-6061
Gecko's Grill & Pub	351 N Cattlemen Rd	378-0077
Gentile Cheesesteaks	7523 S Tamiami Trl	926-0441
Gilligan's Island Bar	5253 Ocean Blvd	349-4759
Grillsmith's	6240 S Tamiami Trl	259-8383
GROVE Restaurant	10670 Boardwalk Lp	893-4321
Gulf Gate Food & Beer	6528 Superior Ave	952-3361
Harry's Continental Kit.	525 St Judes Dr	383-0777
Hob Nob Drive-In	1701 Washington Blvd	955-5001
The Hub Baha Grill	5148 Ocean Blvd	349-6800
Indigenous	239 Links Ave	706-4740
Island House Tap & Grl.	5110 Ocean Blvd	312-9205
Jack Dusty	1111 Ritz-Carlton Dr	309-2266
Joey D's Chicago Style	3811 Kenny Dr.	378-8900
Joey D's Chicago Style	211 N Tamiami Trl	364-9900
JR's Old Packinghouse	987 S Packinghouse	371-9358
Knick's Tavern & Grill	1818 S Osprey Ave	955-7761
Libby's	1917 S Osprey Ave	487-7300
The Lily Cafe	4832 S Tamiami Trl	554-8700
Lovely Square	6559 Gateway Ave	724-2512
Made	1990 Main St	953-2900
Madfish Grill	4059 Cattlemen Rd	377-3474
Mandeville Beer Garden	428 N Lemon Ave	954-8688
Marina Jack's	2 Marina Plaza	365-4243
Mattison's City Grille	1 N Lemon Ave	330-0440
Mattison's Forty One	7275 S Tamiami Trl	921-3400

AMERICAN		
Restaurant Name	Address	Phone #
Melange	1568 Main St	953-7111
Michael John's	1040 Carlton Arms	747-8032
Michael's On East	1212 East Ave	366-0007
Millie's Cafe	3900 Clark Rd	923-4054
Munchies 420 Café	6639 Superior Ave	929-9893
99 Bottles Taproom	1445 2nd St	487-7874
Nancy's Bar-B-Que	14475 SR 70	999-2390
New Pass Grill	1505 Ken Thompson	388-3050
Nicky's Bistro	49 S Palm Ave	330-1727
Oak & Stone	5405 University Pkwy	225-4590
Oak & Stone	4067 Clark Rd	893-4881
Oasis Cafe	3542 S Osprey Ave	957-1214
The Old Salty Dog	5023 Ocean Blvd	349-0158
The Old Salty Dog	160 Ken Thompson Pk	388-4311
The Old Salty Dog	1485 S Tamiami Trl	483-1000
O'Leary's Tiki Bar	5 Bayfront Dr	953-7505
Ophelia's on the Bay	9105 Midnight Pass	349-2212
The Overton	1420 Blvd of the Arts	500-9175
Parrot Patio Bar & Grill	3602 Webber St	952-3352
Pastry Art Bakery	1512 Main St	955-7545
Patrick's 1481	1481 Main St	955-1481
Pier 22	1200 1st Avenue W	748-8087
Pizza N' Brew	1507 Main St	359-3894
Pizza N' Brew	6645 Midnight Pass	349-4490
The Point	135 Bayview Dr	218-6114
Pop's Sunset Grill	112 Circuit Rd	488-3177
The Public House	6240 N Lockwood Rg	822-0795

AMERICAN		
Restaurant Name	**Address**	**Phone #**
The Rosemary	411 N Orange Ave	955-7600
Rosemary & Thyme	511 N Orange Ave	955-7600
Sage	1216 1st St	445-5660
The Sandbar	100 Spring Ave	778-0444
Sarasota Brewing Comp	6607 Gateway Ave	925-2337
Sharky's on the Pier	1600 Harbor Dr S	488-1456
Shore Diner	465 John Ringling Blvd	296-0303
Siesta Key Oyster Bar	5238 Ocean Blvd	346-5443
Smoqehouse	6112 S Tamiami Trl	923-9090
Snook Haven	500 E Venice Ave	485-7221
State St. Eating House	1533 State St	951-1533
Station 400	400 Lemon Ave	906-1400
Station 400	8215 Lakewood Main	907-0648
Stottlemeyer's Smokehs	19 East Rd	312-5969
Sun Garden Cafe	210 Avenida Madera	346-7170
Sunnyside Cafe	4900 N Tamiami Trl	359-9500
Tasty Home Cookin'	3854 S Tuttle Ave	921-4969
Toasted Mango Café	6621 Midnight Pass	552-6485
Toasted Mango Café	430 N Tamiami Trl	388-7728
Tommy Bahama Café	300 John Ringling Blvd	388-2888
Tony's Chicago Beef	6569 Superior Ave	922-7979
Turtle's	8875 Midnight Pass	346-2207
Village Café	5133 Ocean Blvd	349-2822
The Whiskey Barrel	15 S Blvd of Pres.	266-9650
Word of Mouth	6604 Gateway Ave	925-2400
Yoder's Restaurant	3434 Bahia Vista	955-7771

ASIAN		
Restaurant Name	Address	Phone #
Bushido Izayaki	3688 Webber St	217-5635
DaRuMa Japanese	5459 Fruitville Rd	342-6600
DaRuMa Japanese	4910 S. Tamiami Trl	552-9465
Dim Sum King	8194 Tourist Center Dr	306-5848
Drunken Poet Café	1572 Main St	955-8404
Hoshi Sushi	6516 Superior Ave	923-8888
Jpan Sushi & Grill	3 Paradise Plaza	954-5726
Jpan Sushi & Grill	229 N Cattlemen Rd	954-5726
Kiyoski's Sushi	6550 Gateway Ave	924-3781
Kojo	1289 N Palm Ave	536-9717
Korean Ssam Bar	1303 N Washington	312-6264
Little Saigon Bistro	2725 S Beneva Rd	312-4730
Pacific Rim	1859 Hillview St	330-8071
Pho Cali	1578 Main St	955-2683
Spice Station	1438 Blvd of the Arts	343-2894
Star Thai & Sushi	935 N Beneva Rd	706-3848
Star Thai & Sushi	240 Avenida Madera	217-6758
Stiks	4413 S Tamiami Trl	923-2742
Taste of Hong Kong	2224 Gulf Gate Dr	922-6765
Yume Sushi	1532 Main St	363-0604
Yummy House	1737 S Tamiami Trl	351-1688

CUBAN, MEXICAN & SPANISH		
Bohemios Tapas Bar	3246 Clark Rd	260-9784
Circo	1435 2nd St	253-0978
The Columbia	411 St Armands Cir	388-3987
El Melvin Cocina	1355 Main St	366-1618
El Toro Bravo	2720 Stickney Pt Rd	924-0006

CUBAN, MEXICAN & SPANISH

Restaurant Name	Address	Phone #
The Grasshopper	7253 S Tamiami Trl	923-3688
Island House Taqueria	2773 Bee Ridge Rd	922-8226
Poppo's Taqueria	4990 S Tamiami Trl	343-2341
Reyna's Taqueria	935 N Beneva Rd	260-8343
Screaming Goat Taq.	6606 Superior Ave	210-3992
Wicked Cantina	1603 N Tamiami Trl	821-2990

DELI

Anna's Deli	6535 Midnight Pass	348-4888
Cafe in the Park	2010 Adams Ln	361-3032
Gentile Cheesesteaks	7523 S Tamiami Trl	926-0441
Main Bar Sandwich Shp	1944 Main St	955-8733
Michelle's Brown Bag	1819 Main St	365-5858
Nellie's Deli	15 S Beneva Rd	924-2705
Piccolo Italian Market	6518 Gateway Ave	923-2202
Simon's Coffee House	5900 S Tamiami Trl	926-7151
S Philly Cheesesteaks	1439 Main St	330-8208
Southside Deli	1825 Hillview St	330-9302

ENGLISH, IRISH & SCOTTISH

Irish 31	3750 S Tamiami Trl	234-9265
Pub 32	8383 S Tamiami Trl	952-3070
Shakespeare's Eng Pub	3550 S Osprey Ave	364-5938

FRENCH

A Sprig of Thyme	1962 Hillview St	330-8890
Bonjour French Cafe	5214 Ocean Blvd	346-0600
Café Longet	239 Miami Ave W	244-2643

FRENCH		
Restaurant Name	**Address**	**Phone #**
C'est La Vie!	1553 Main St	906-9575
Figaro Bistro	1944 Hillview St	960-2109
Mademoiselle Paris	8527 Cooper Creek Bl	355-2323
Maison Blanche	2605 Gulf of Mexico Dr	383-8088
Miguel's	6631 Midnight Pass	349-4024
Rendez-Vous Bakery	5336 Clark Rd	924-1234

GREEK		
Apollonia Grill	8235 Cooper Creek	359-4816
Athen's Family Rest.	2300 Bee Ridge Rd	706-4121
Blu Kouzina	25 N Blvd of Pres	388-2619
1592 Wood Fired Kitch	1592 Main St	365-2234

INDIAN		
Curry Station	3550 Clark Rd	924-7222
Rasoi Indian Kitchen	7119 S Tamiami Trl	921-9200

ITALIAN		
Amore	180 N Lime Ave	383-1111
Andrea's	2085 Siesta Dr	951-9200
Atmosphere	935 N Beneva Rd	203-8542
Bevardi's Salute!	23 N Lemon Ave	365-1020
Cafe Baci	4001 S. Tamiami Trl	921-4848
Café Barbosso	5501 Palmer Crossing	922-7999
Café Epicure	1298 Main St	366-5648
Café Gabbiano	5104 Ocean Blvd	349-1423
Café L'Europe	431 St Armands Cir	388-4415

ITALIAN		
Restaurant Name	Address	Phone #
Caragiulos	69 S Palm Ave	951-0866
Cassariano Italian Eat.	313 W Venice Ave	485-0507
Clasico Italian Chophse	1341 Main St	957-0700
Dolce Italia	6606 Superior Ave	921-7007
Flavio's Brick Oven	5239 Ocean Blvd	349-0995
La Norma	5370 Gulf of Mexico Dr	383-6262
Marcello's Ristorante	4155 S Tamiami Trl	921-6794
Mediterraneo	1970 Main St	365-4122
Napule Ristorante	7129 S Tamiami Trl	556-9639
Pazzo Southside	1936 Hillview St	260-8831
Piccolo Italian Market	6518 Gateway Ave	923-2202
Sardinia	5770 S Tamiami Trl	702-8582
Shaner's Pizza	6500 Superior Ave	927-2708

SEAFOOD		
Anna Maria Oyster Bar	6906 14th St W	758-7880
Anna Maria Oyster Bar	6696 Cortez Rd	792-0077
Big Water Fish Market	6641 Midgnight Pass	554-8101
Brine Seafood	2250 Gulf Gate Dr	404-5639
Capt. Brian's Seafood	8421 N Tamiami Trl	351-4492
Capt. Curt's Oyster Bar	1200 Old Stickney Pt	349-3885
Casey Key Fish House	801 Blackburn Pt Rd	966-1901
Crab & Fin	420 St Armands Cir	388-3964
The Crow's Nest	1968 Tarpon Ctr Dr	484-9551
Dry Dock Waterfront	412 Gulf of Mexico Dr	383-0102
Duval's, Fresh, Local...	1435 Main St	312-4001
Fins At Sharky's	1600 Harbor Dr S	999-3467

SEAFOOD

Restaurant Name	Address	Phone #
Lazy Lobster	5350 Gulf of Mexico Dr	388-0440
Lazy Lobster	7602 N Lockwood Rg	351-5515
The Lobster Pot	5157 Ocean Blvd	349-2323
Mar-Vista Restaurant	760 Broadway St	383-2391
Monk's Steamer Bar	6690 Superior Ave	927-3388
Ophelia's on the Bay	9105 Midnight Pass	349-2212
Owen's Fish Camp	516 Burns Ct	951-6936
Phillippi Creek Oyster	5363 S Tamiami Trl	925-4444
Reef Cakes	1812 S Osprey Ave	444-7968
The Sandbar	100 Spring Ave	778-0444
Siesta Key Oyster Bar	5238 Ocean Blvd	346-5443
Speaks Clam Bar	29 N Blvd of Pres.	232-7633
Spear Fish Grille	1265 Old Stickney Pt	349-1970
Tripletail Seafood	4870 S Tamiami Trl	529-0555
Veronica Fish & Oyster	1830 S Osprey Ave	366-1342
Walt's Fish Market	4144 S Tamiami Trl	921-4605

STEAKHOUSE

Connors Steakhouse	3501 S Tamiami Trl	260-3232
Element	1413 Main St	724-8585
Fleming's Steakhouse	2001 Siesta Dr	358-9463
Karl Ehmer's Alpine	4520 S Tamiami Trl	922-3797
Rosebud's Steakhouse	2215 S Tamiami Trl	918-8771
Ruth's Chris Steakhouse	6700 S Tamiami Trl	942-9442
Summer House	149 Avenida Messina	206-2675

ANNA MARIA, BRADENTON, & PALMETTO		
Restaurant Name	Address	Phone #
Beach Bistro	6600 Gulf Dr N	778-6444
The Beach House	200 Gulf Dr N	779-2222
Bridge Street Bistro	111 Gulf Dr S	782-1122
Michael John's	1040 Carlton Arms	747-8032
Pier 22	1200 1st Avenue W	748-8087
The Sandbar	100 Spring Ave	778-0444

DOWNTOWN		
Amore	180 N Lime Ave	383-1111
Bavaro's Pizza	27 Fletcher Ave	552-9131
Bevardi's Salute!	23 N Lemon Ave	365-1020
Bijou Cafe	1287 First St	366-8111
Blue Rooster	1524 Fourth St	388-5739
Boca Kitchen, Bar, Mkt	21 S Lemon Ave	256-3565
The Bodhi Tree	1938 Adams Ln	702-8552
The Breakfast House	1817 Fruitville Rd	366-6860
Brick's Smoked Meats	1528 State St	993-1435
Café Epicure	1298 Main St	366-5648
Cafe in the Park	2010 Adams Ln	361-3032
Cask & Ale	1548 Main St	702-8740
Caragiulos	69 S Palm Ave	951-0866
C'est La Vie!	1553 Main St	906-9575
Circo	1435 2nd St	253-0978
Clasico Italian Chophse	1341 Main St	957-0700
Doggystyle	1544 Main St	260-5835
Drunken Poet Café	1572 Main St	955-8404
Duval's, Fresh, Local...	1435 Main St	312-4001

DOWNTOWN		
Restaurant Name	Address	Phone #
El Melvin Cocina	1355 Main St	366-1618
Element	1413 Main St	724-8585
EVOQ	1175 N. Gulfstream	260-8255
1592 Wood Fired Kitch	1592 Main St	365-2234
Il Panificio	1703 Main St	366-5570
Indigenous	239 Links Ave	706-4740
Jack Dusty	1111 Ritz-Carlton Dr	309-2266
Kojo	1289 N Palm Ave	536-9717
Lila	1576 Main St	296-1042
Made	1990 Main St	953-2900
Main Bar Sandwich Shp	1944 Main St	955-8733
Mandeville Beer Garden	428 N Lemon Ave	954-8688
Marina Jack's	2 Marina Plaza	365-4243
Mattison's City Grille	1 N Lemon Ave	330-0440
Mediterraneo	1970 Main St	365-4122
Melange	1568 Main St	953-7111
Michelle's Brown Bag	1819 Main St	365-5858
99 Bottles Taproom	1445 2nd St	487-7874
Nicky's Bistro	49 S Palm Ave	330-1727
O'Leary's Tiki Bar	5 Bayfront Dr	953-7505
The Overton	1420 Blvd of the Arts	500-9175
Owen's Fish Camp	516 Burns Ct	951-6936
Pastry Art Bakery	1512 Main St	955-7545
Patrick's 1481	1481 Main St	955-1481
Pho Cali	1578 Main St	955-2683
Pizza N' Brew	1507 Main St	359-3894
The Rosemary	411 N Orange Ave	955-7600
Rosemary & Thyme	511 N Orange Ave	955-7600

DOWNTOWN		
Restaurant Name	**Address**	**Phone #**
Sage	1216 1st St	445-5660
Selva Grill	1345 Main St	362-4427
Siegfried's Restaurant	1869 Fruitville Rd	330-9330
S Philly Cheesesteaks	1439 Main St	330-8208
Spice Station	1438 Blvd of the Arts	343-2894
State St Eating House	1533 State St	951-1533
Station 400	400 Lemon Ave	906-1400
Yume Sushi	1532 Main St	363-0604

GULF GATE		
Brine Seafood	2250 Gulf Gate Dr	404-5639
Dix Coney Cafe	6525 Superior Ave	927-1672
Dolce Italia	6606 Superior Ave	921-7007
Gulf Gate Food & Beer	6528 Superior Ave	952-3361
Hoshi Sushi	6516 Superior Ave	923-8888
Kiyoski's Sushi	6550 Gateway Ave	924-3781
Lovely Square	6559 Gateway Ave	724-2512
Monk's Steamer Bar	6690 Superior Ave	927-3388
Munchies 420 Café	6639 Superior Ave	929-9893
Piccolo Italian Market	6518 Gateway Ave	923-2202
RomanSQ Pizza	6670 Superior Ave	237-8742
Sarasota Brewing Comp	6607 Gateway Ave	925-2337
Schnitzel Kitchen	6521 Superior Ave	922-9299
Screaming Goat Taq.	6606 Superior Ave	210-3992
Shaner's Pizza	6500 Superior Ave	927-2708
Taste of Hong Kong	2224 Gulf Gate Dr	922-6765
Tony's Chicago Beef	6569 Superior Ave	922-7979

GULF GATE

Restaurant Name	Address	Phone #
Veg	2164 Gulf Gate Dr	312-6424
Word of Mouth	6604 Gateway Ave	925-2400

LONGBOAT KEY & LIDO KEY

Drift Kitchen	700 Benjamin Franklin	388-2161
Dry Dock Waterfront	412 Gulf of Mexico Dr	383-0102
Euphemia Haye	5540 Gulf of Mexico Dr	383-3633
Lazy Lobster	5350 Gulf of Mexico Dr	388-0440
Harry's Continental Kit.	525 St Judes Dr	383-0777
La Norma	5370 Gulf of Mexico Dr	383-6262
Maison Blanche	2605 Gulf of Mexico Dr	383-8088
Mar-Vista Restaurant	760 Broadway St	383-2391
New Pass Grill	1505 Ken Thompson	388-3050

LAKEWOOD RANCH & UNIVERSITY PARK

Apollonia Grill	8235 Cooper Creek	359-4816
Dim Sum King	8194 Tourist Center Dr	306-5848
GROVE Restaurant	10670 Boardwalk Lp	893-4321
Inkawasi Peruvian	10667 Boardwalk Lp	360-1110
Jpan Sushi & Grill	229 N Cattlemen Rd	954-5726
Mademoiselle Paris	8527 Cooper Creek Bl	355-2323
Main Street Trattoria	8131 Lakewood Main	907-1518
Nancy's Bar-B-Que	14475 SR 70	999-2390
Oak & Stone	5405 University Pkwy	225-4590

NORTH TAMIAMI TRAIL		
Restaurant Name	Address	Phone #
Capt. Brian's Seafood	8421 N Tamiami Trl	351-4492
Hob Nob Drive-In	1701 Washington Blvd	955-5001
Sunnyside Cafe	4900 N Tamiami Trl	359-9500
Toasted Mango Café	430 N Tamiami Trl	388-7728
Wicked Cantina	1603 N Tamiami Trl	821-2990

ST. ARMANDS KEY		
Blu Kouzina	25 N Blvd of Pres	388-2619
Café L'Europe	431 St Armands Cir	388-4415
Cha Cha Coconuts	417 St Armands Cir	388-3300
The Columbia	411 St Armands Cir	388-3987
Crab & Fin	420 St Armands Cir	388-3964
Shore Diner	465 John Ringling Blvd	296-0303
Speaks Clam Bar	29 N Blvd of Pres	232-7633
Tommy Bahama Cafe	300 John Ringling Blvd	388-2888
The Whiskey Barrel	15 S Blvd of Pres.	266-9650

SIESTA KEY		
Anna's Deli	6535 Midnight Pass	348-4888
Big Water Fish Market	6641 Midgnight Pass	554-8101
Bonjour French Cafe	5214 Ocean Blvd	346-0600
Café Gabbiano	5104 Ocean Blvd	349-1423
Capt. Curt's Oyster Bar	1200 Old Stickney Pt	349-3885
Clayton's Siesta Grille	1256 Old Stickney Pt	349-2800
The Cottage	153 Avenida Messina	312-9300
Daiquiri Deck Raw Bar	5250 Ocean Blvd	349-8697
Flavio's Brick Oven	5239 Ocean Blvd	349-0995

SIESTA KEY		
Restaurant Name	**Address**	**Phone #**
Gilligan's Island Bar	5253 Ocean Blvd	349-4759
The Hub Baha Grill	5148 Ocean Blvd	349-6800
Il Panificio	215 Avenida Madera	800-5570
Island House Tap & Grl.	5110 Ocean Blvd	312-9205
The Lobster Pot	5157 Ocean Blvd	349-2323
Miguel's	6631 Midnight Pass	349-4024
The Old Salty Dog	5023 Ocean Blvd	349-0158
Ophelia's on the Bay	9105 Midnight Pass	349-2212
Ripfire Pizza & BBQ	5218 Ocean Blvd	313-7511
Siesta Key Oyster Bar	5238 Ocean Blvd	346-5443
Spear Fish Grille	1265 Old Stickney Pt	349-1970
Star Thai & Sushi	240 Avenida Madera	217-6758
Summer House	149 Avenida Messina	206-2675
Sun Garden Café	210 Avenida Madera	346-7170
Toasted Mango Café	6621 Midnight Pass	552-6485
Turtle's	8875 Midnight Pass	346-2207
Village Café	5133 Ocean Blvd	349-2822

SOUTH TAMIAMI TRAIL		
Almazonica Cerveceria	4141 S Tamiami Trl	260-5964
Breakfast at Victoria's	4141 S Tamiami Trl	923-6441
Cafe Baci	4001 S. Tamiami Trl	921-4848
Connors Steakhouse	3501 S Tamiami Trl	260-3232
DaRuMa Japanese	4910 S. Tamiami Trl	552-9465
Dutch Valley Rest.	6731 S Tamiami Trl	924-1770
Gecko's Grill & Pub	4870 S Tamiami Trl	923-8896

SOUTH TAMIAMI TRAIL

Restaurant Name	Address	Phone #
Gentile Cheesesteaks	7523 S Tamiami Trl	926-0441
The Grasshopper	7253 S Tamiami Trl	923-3688
Grillsmith's	6240 S Tamiami Trl	259-8383
Irish 31	3750 S Tamiami Trl	234-9265
Karl Ehmer's Alpine	4520 S Tamiami Trl	922-3797
The Lily Cafe	4832 S Tamiami Trl	554-8700
Marcello's Ristorante	4155 S Tamiami Trl	921-6794
Mattison's Forty One	7275 S Tamiami Trl	921-3400
Michael's On East	1212 East Ave	366-0007
Napule Ristorante	7129 S Tamiami Trl	556-9639
Poppo's Taqueria	4990 S Tamiami Trl	343-2341
Phillippi Creek Oyster	5363 S Tamiami Trl	925-4444
Pub 32	8383 S Tamiami Trl	952-3070
Rasoi Indian Kitchen	7119 S Tamiami Trl	921-9200
Roessler's	2033 Vamo Way	966-5688
Ruth's Chris Steakhouse	6700 S Tamiami Trl	942-9442
Sardinia	5770 S Tamiami Trl	702-8582
Stiks	4413 S Tamiami Trl	923-2742
Simon's Coffee House	5900 S Tamiami Trl	926-7151
Smoqehouse	6112 S Tamiami Trl	923-9090
Tripletail Seafood	4870 S Tamiami Trl	529-0555
Walt's Fish Market	4144 S Tamiami Trl	921-4605
Yummy House	1737 S Tamiami Trl	351-1688

SOUTHSIDE VILLAGE

A Sprig of Thyme	1962 Hillview St	330-8890
Figaro Bistro	1944 Hillview St	960-2109

SOUTHSIDE VILLAGE

Restaurant Name	Address	Phone #
Ka Papa Vegan	1830 S Osprey Ave	600-8590
Knick's Tavern & Grill	1818 S Osprey Ave	955-7761
Libby's Brasserie	1917 S Osprey Ave	487-7300
Origin Beer & Pizza	3837 Hillview St	316-9222
Pacific Rim	1859 Hillview St	330-8071
Pazzo Southside	1830 S Osprey Ave	260-8831
Reef Cakes	1812 S Osprey Ave	444-7968
Southside Deli	1825 Hillview St	330-9302
Veronica Fish & Oyster	1830 S Osprey Ave	366-1342

SOUTHGATE

Andrea's	2085 Siesta Dr	951-9200
Baker & Wife	2157 Siesta Dr	960-1765
Connors Steakhouse	3501 S Tamiami Trl	260-3232
Fleming's Steakhouse	2001 Siesta Dr	358-9463

UNIVERSITY TOWN CENTER (UTC)

Brio Tuscan Grille	190 Univ Town Ctr Dr	702-9102
Burger & Beer Joint	160 Univ Town Ctr Dr	702-9915
The Capital Grille	180 Univ Town Ctr Dr	256-3647
Cheesecake Factory	130 Univ Town Ctr Dr	256-3760
Kona Grill	150 Univ Town Ctr Dr	256-8005
Rise Pies Pizza	140 Univ Town Ctr Dr	702-9920
Seasons 52	170 Univ Town Ctr Dr	702-9652
Sophies	120 Univ Town Ctr Dr	444-3077

LIVE MUSIC		
Restaurant Name	Address	Phone #
Blue Rooster	1524 Fourth St	388-5739
Capt. Curt's Oyster Bar	1200 Old Stickney Pt	349-3885
Casey Key Fish House	801 Blackburn Pt Rd	966-1901
Gecko's Grill & Pub	4870 S Tamiami Trl	923-8896
Gilligan's Island Bar	5253 Ocean Blvd	349-4759
The Hub Baha Grill	5148 Ocean Blvd	349-6800
JR's Old Packinghouse	987 S Packinghouse	371-9358
Marina Jack's	2 Marina Plaza	365-4243
Mattison's City Grille	1 N Lemon Ave	330-0440
Mattison's Forty One	7275 S Tamiami Trl	921-3400
Nancy's Bar-B-Que	14475 SR 70	999-2390
Nicky's Bistro	49 S Palm Ave	330-1727
O'Leary's Tiki Bar	5 Bayfront Dr	953-7505
Parrot Patio Bar & Grill	3602 Webber St	952-3352
Pop's Sunset Grill	112 Circuit Rd	488-3177
Sharky's on the Pier	1600 Harbor Dr S	488-1456
Siesta Key Oyster Bar	5238 Ocean Blvd	346-5443
Star Thai & Sushi	240 Avenida Madera	217-6758
Stottlemeyer's Smokehs	19 East Rd	312-5969
Walt's Fish Market	4144 S Tamiami Trl	921-4605

CATERING		
The Beach House	200 Gulf Dr N	779-2222
Brick's Smoked Meats	1528 State St	993-1435
Daiquiri Deck Raw Bar	5250 Ocean Blvd	349-8697
Gecko's Grill & Pub	4870 S Tamiami Trl	923-8896
Harry's Continental Kit.	525 St Judes Dr	383-0777
JR's Old Packinghouse	987 S Packinghouse	371-9358

CATERING		
Restaurant Name	**Address**	**Phone #**
Mattison's Forty One	7275 S Tamiami Trl	921-3400
Michael's On East	1212 East Ave	366-0007
Nancy's Bar-B-Que	301 S Pineapple Ave	366-2271
Nellie's Deli	15 S Beneva Rd	924-2705
Village Café	5133 Ocean Blvd	349-2822

EASY ON YOUR WALLET		
Athen's Family Rest.	2300 Bee Ridge Rd	706-4121
Anna's Deli	6535 Midnight Pass	348-4888
Breakfast at Victoria's	4141 S Tamiami Trl	923-6441
The Breakfast House	1817 Fruitville Rd	366-6860
Cafe in the Park	2010 Adams Ln	361-3032
Casey Key Fish House	801 Blackburn Pt Rd	966-1901
Circo	1435 2nd St	253-0978
Dim Sum King	8194 Tourist Center Dr	306-5848
Dix Coney Cafe	6525 Superior Ave	927-1672
Doggystyle	1544 Main St	260-5835
Dutch Valley Rest.	6731 S Tamiami Trl	924-1770
El Toro Bravo	2720 Stickney Pt	924-0006
Gentile Cheesesteaks	7523 S Tamiami Trl	926-0441
Hob Nob Drive-In	1701 Washington Blvd	955-5001
Il Panificio	1703 Main St	366-5570
Island House Taqueria	2773 Bee Ridge Rd	922-8226
Joey D's Chicago Style	3811 Kenny Dr.	378-8900
Joey D's Chicago Style	211 N Tamiami Trl	364-9900
L&L Hawaiian Barbecue	5445 Fruitville Rd	315-9008
Little Saigon Bistro	2725 S Beneva Rd	312-4730

EASY ON YOUR WALLET		
Restaurant Name	**Address**	**Phone #**
Lovely Square	6559 Gateway Ave	724-2512
Main Bar Sandwich Shp	1944 Main St	955-8733
Michelle's Brown Bag	1819 Main St	365-5858
Munchies 420 Café	6639 Superior Ave	929-9893
New Pass Grill	1505 Ken Thompson	388-3050
Pastry Art Bakery	1512 Main St	955-7545
Pho Cali	1578 Main St	955-2683
Piccolo Italian Market	6518 Gateway Ave	923-2202
Poppo's Taqueria	4990 S Tamiami Trl	343-2341
Rendez-Vous Bakery	5336 Clark Rd	924-1234
Reyna's Taqueria	935 N Beneva Rd	260-8343
Rico's Pizza - Bay Rd	1902 Bay Rd	366-8988
Screaming Goat Taq.	6606 Superior Ave	210-3992
Shaner's Pizza	6500 Superior Ave	927-2708
Smoqehouse	6112 S Tamiami Trl	923-9090
Simon's Coffee House	5900 S Tamiami Trl	926-7151
Stiks	4413 S Tamiami Trl	923-2742
S Philly Cheesesteaks	1439 Main St	330-8208
Southside Deli	1825 Hillview St	330-9302
Sunnyside Cafe	4900 N Tamiami Trl	359-9500
Tasty Home Cookin'	3854 S Tuttle Ave	921-4969
Tony's Chicago Beef	6569 Superior Ave	922-7979
Yoder's Restaurant	3434 Bahia Vista	955-7771
Wicked Cantina	1603 N Tamiami Trl	821-2990
BREAKFAST & LUNCH		
Anna's Deli	6535 Midnight Pass	348-4888
Bonjour French Cafe	5214 Ocean Blvd	346-0600

BREAKFAST & LUNCH		
Restaurant Name	Address	Phone #
Breakfast at Victoria's	4141 S Tamiami Trl	923-6441
The Breakfast House	1817 Fruitville Rd	366-6860
Cafe in the Park	2010 Adams Ln	361-3032
The Lily Cafe	4832 S Tamiami Trl	554-8700
Lovely Square	6559 Gateway Ave	724-2512
Main Bar Sandwich Shp	1944 Main St	955-8733
Michelle's Brown Bag	1819 Main St	365-5858
Millie's Cafe	3900 Clark Rd	923-4054
Nellie's Deli	15 S Beneva Rd	924-2705
Oasis Cafe	3542 S Osprey Ave	957-1214
Pastry Art Bakery	1512 Main St	955-7545
Rendez-Vous Bakery	5336 Clark Rd	924-1234
The Rosemary	411 N Orange Ave	955-7600
Simon's Coffee House	5900 S Tamiami Trl	926-7151
Southside Deli	1825 Hillview St	330-9302
Station 400	400 Lemon Ave	906-1400
Sun Garden Café	210 Avenida Madera	346-7170
Sunnyside Cafe	4900 N Tamiami Trl	359-9500
Tasty Home Cookin'	3854 S Tuttle Ave	921-4969
Toasted Mango Café	6621 Midnight Pass	552-6485
Village Café	5133 Ocean Blvd	349-2822
Word of Mouth	6604 Gateway Ave	925-2400
NEW		
Almazonica Cerveceria	4141 S Tamiami Trl	260-5964
Atmosphere	935 N Beneva Rd	203-8542
Bohemios Tapas Bar	3246 Clark Rd	260-9784
The Breakfast House	1817 Fruitville Rd	366-6860

NEW		
Restaurant Name	**Address**	**Phone #**
Dim Sum King	8194 Tourist Center Dr	306-5848
Dix Coney Cafe	6525 Superior Ave	927-1672
Doggystyle	1544 Main St	260-5835
El Melvin Cocina	1355 Main St	366-1618
Figaro Bistro	1944 Hillview St	960-2109
Hoshi Sushi	6516 Superior Ave	923-8888
Ka Papa Vegan	1830 S Osprey Ave	600-8590
Kojo	1289 N Palm Ave	536-9717
L&L Hawaiian Barbecue	5445 Fruitville Rd	315-9008
La Norma	5370 Gulf of Mexico Dr	383-6262
The Lily Cafe	4832 S Tamiami Trl	554-8700
Little Saigon Bistro	2725 S Beneva Rd	312-4730
Nicky's Bistro	49 S Palm Ave	330-1727
Pizza N' Brew	1507 Main St	359-3894
The Public House	6240 N Lockwood Rg	822-0795
RomanSQ Pizza	6670 Superior Ave	237-8742
Stiks	4413 S Tamiami Trl	923-2742
Tripletail Seafood	4870 S Tamiami Trl	529-0555
The Whiskey Barrel	15 S Blvd of Pres.	266-9650

SUSHI		
Bushido Izayaki	3688 Webber St	217-5635
DaRuMa Japanese	5459 Fruitville Rd	342-6600
DaRuMa Japanese	4910 S. Tamiami Trl	552-9465
Drunken Poet Café	1572 Main St	955-8404
Hoshi Sushi	6516 Superior Ave	923-8888
Jpan Sushi & Grill	3 Paradise Plaza	954-5726
Jpan Sushi & Grill	229 N Cattlemen Rd	954-5726

SUSHI		
Restaurant Name	**Address**	**Phone #**
Kiyoski's Sushi	6550 Gateway Ave	924-3781
Kojo	1289 N Palm Ave	536-9717
Pacific Rim	1859 Hillview St	330-8071
Spice Station	1438 Blvd of the Arts	343-2894
Star Thai & Sushi	935 N Beneva Rd	706-3848
Star Thai & Sushi	240 Avenida Madera	217-6758
Yume Sushi	1532 Main St	363-0604

SPORTS + FOOD + FUN		
Capt. Curt's Oyster Bar	1200 Old Stickney Pt	349-3885
Daiquiri Deck Raw Bar	5250 Ocean Blvd	349-8697
Gecko's Grill & Pub	6606 S Tamiami Trl	248-2020
Gecko's Grill & Pub	1900 Hillview St	953-2929
Gecko's Grill & Pub	5588 Palmer Crossing	923-6061
Oak & Stone	5405 University Pkwy	225-4590
The Old Salty Dog	5023 Ocean Blvd	349-0158
Parrot Patio Bar & Grill	3602 Webber St	952-3352
Patrick's 1481	1481 Main St	955-1481
Siesta Key Oyster Bar	5238 Ocean Blvd	346-5443

GREAT BURGERS		
Cask & Ale	1548 Main St	702-8740
Cha Cha Coconuts	417 St Armands Cir	388-3300
Connors Steakhouse	3501 S. Tamiami Trl	260-3232
Daiquiri Deck Raw Bar	5250 Ocean Blvd	349-8697
Daiquiri Deck Raw Bar	325 John Ringling Blvd	388-3325
Daiquiri Deck Raw Bar	300 W Venice Ave	488-0649
Daiquiri Deck Raw Bar	1250 Stickney Pt Rd	312-2422

GREAT BURGERS		
Restaurant Name	Address	Phone #
Dix Coney Cafe	6525 Superior Ave	927-1672
Gecko's Grill & Pub	4870 S Tamiami Trl	923-8896
Gecko's Grill & Pub	1900 Hillview St	953-2929
Gecko's Grill & Pub	5588 Palmer Crossing	923-6061
Gecko's Grill & Pub	351 N Cattlemen Rd	378-0077
Gulf Gate Food & Beer	6528 Superior Ave	952-3361
Hob Nob Drive-In	1701 Washington Blvd	955-5001
Indigenous	239 Links Ave	706-4740
Island House Tap & Grl.	5110 Ocean Blvd	312-9205
Joey D's Chicago Style	3811 Kenny Dr.	378-8900
Joey D's Chicago Style	211 N Tamiami Trl	364-9900
JR's Old Packinghouse	987 S Packinghouse	371-9358
Karl Ehmer's Alpine	4520 S Tamiami Trl	922-3797
Knick's Tavern & Grill	1818 S Osprey Ave	955-7761
Libby's Brasserie	1917 S Osprey Ave	487-7300
Made	1990 Main St	953-2900
Munchies 420 Café	6639 Superior Ave	929-9893
New Pass Grill	1505 Ken Thompson	388-3050
Parrot Patio Bar & Grill	3602 Webber St	952-3352
Patrick's 1481	1481 Main St	955-1481
Pop's Sunset Grill	112 Circuit Rd	488-3177
The Public House	6240 N Lockwood Rg	822-0795
Shakespeare's Eng Pub	3550 S Osprey Ave	364-5938
Sharky's on the Pier	1600 Harbor Dr S	488-1456
Tasty Home Cookin'	3854 S Tuttle Ave	921-4969
Tony's Chicago Beef	6569 Superior Ave	922-7979
Village Café	5133 Ocean Blvd	349-2822

NICE WINE LIST		
Restaurant Name	**Address**	**Phone #**
Amore	180 N Lime Ave	383-1111
Andrea's	2085 Siesta Dr	951-9200
Baker & Wife	2157 Siesta Dr	960-1765
Beach Bistro	6600 Gulf Dr N	778-6444
Bevardi's Salute!	23 N Lemon Ave	365-1020
Bijou Café	1287 First St	366-8111
Café Barbosso	5501 Palmer Crossing	922-7999
Café Gabbiano	5104 Ocean Blvd	349-1423
Café L'Europe	431 St Armands Cir	388-4415
Café Longet	239 Miami Ave W	244-2643
Cassariano Italian Eat.	313 W Venice Ave	485-0507
Connors Steakhouse	3501 S Tamiami Trl	260-3232
Dolce Italia	6606 Superior Ave	921-7007
Duval's, Fresh, Local...	1435 Main St	312-4001
Element	1413 Main St	724-8585
Euphemia Haye	5540 Gulf of Mexico Dr	383-3633
Figaro Bistro	1944 Hillview St	960-2109
Fins At Sharky's	1600 Harbor Dr S	999-3467
Flavio's Brick Oven	5239 Ocean Blvd	349-0995
GROVE Restaurant	10670 Boardwalk Lp	893-4321
Harry's Continental Kit.	525 St Judes Dr	383-0777
Indigenous	239 Links Ave	706-4740
Jack Dusty	1111 Ritz-Carlton Dr	309-2266
Maison Blanche	2605 Gulf of Mexico Dr	383-8088
Mattison's Forty One	7275 S Tamiami Trl	921-3400
Melange	1568 Main St	953-7111
Michael John's	1040 Carlton Arms	747-8032

NICE WINE LIST		
Restaurant Name	Address	Phone #
Michael's On East	1212 East Ave	366-0007
Miguel's	6631 Midnight Pass	349-4024
Napule Ristorante	7129 S Tamiami Trl	556-9639
Ophelia's on the Bay	9105 Midnight Pass	349-2212
Pier 22	1200 1st Avenue W	748-8087
Roessler's	2033 Vamo Way	966-5688
Rosebud's Steakhouse	2215 S Tamiami Trl	918-8771
Rosemary & Thyme	511 N Orange Ave	955-7600
Sage	1216 1st St	445-5660
Sardinia	5770 S Tamiami Trl	702-8582
State St Eating House	1533 State St	951-1533
Summer House	149 Avenida Messina	206-2675

HELP MAKE A DIFFERENCE IN OUR SARASOTA-MANATEE COMMUNITY

Listed below are two local organizations that are striving to assist those in need in our Sarasota area. They could use your help. Please consider a donation to either (or both) during 2022.

ALL FAITHS FOOD BANK
WHAT THEY NEED: Donations of non-perishable, frozen, and perishable food items needed. Monetary donations are also accepted and can be made directly through their website.
MORE INFO: allfaithsfoodbank.org

MAYOR'S FEED THE HUNGRY PROGRAM
WHAT THEY NEED: Donations of food, time, and money are needed. This program hosts a large food drive in the month of November. Check their website for details or to make a monetary donation.
MORE INFO: mayorsfeedthehungry.org

NICE WINE LIST		
Restaurant Name	**Address**	**Phone #**
Selva Grill	1345 Main St	362-4427
Veronica Fish & Oyster	1830 S Osprey Ave	366-1342

A BEAUTIFUL WATER VIEW		
Beach Bistro	6600 Gulf Dr N	778-6444
The Beach House	200 Gulf Dr N	779-2222
Casey Key Fish House	801 Blackburn Pt Rd	966-1901
The Crow's Nest	1968 Tarpon Ctr Dr	484-9551
Drift Kitchen	700 Benjamin Franklin	388-2161
Dry Dock Waterfront	412 Gulf of Mexico Dr	383-0102
Fins At Sharky's	1600 Harbor Dr S	999-3467
Jack Dusty	1111 Ritz-Carlton Dr	309-2266
Mar-Vista Restaurant	760 Broadway St	383-2391
Marina Jack's	2 Marina Plaza	365-4243
New Pass Grill	1505 Ken Thompson	388-3050
The Old Salty Dog	160 Ken Thompson Pk	388-4311
The Old Salty Dog	1485 S Tamiami Trl	483-1000
O'Leary's Tiki Bar	5 Bayfront Dr	953-7505
Ophelia's on the Bay	9105 Midnight Pass	349-2212
Phillippi Creek Oyster	5363 S Tamiami Trl	925-4444
Pier 22	1200 1st Avenue W	748-8087
Pop's Sunset Grill	112 Circuit Rd	488-3177
The Sandbar	100 Spring Ave	778-0444
Sharky's on the Pier	1600 Harbor Dr S	488-1456
Snook Haven	500 E Venice Ave	485-7221
Turtle's	8875 Midnight Pass	346-2207

LATER NIGHT MENU		
Restaurant Name	**Address**	**Phone #**
Blue Rooster	1524 Fourth St	388-5739
Café Epicure	1298 Main St	366-5648
Capt. Curt's Oyster Bar	1200 Old Stickney Pt	349-3885
Casey Key Fish House	801 Blackburn Pt Rd	966-1901
Cask & Ale	1548 Main St	702-8740
Circo	1435 2nd St	253-0978
The Cottage	153 Avenida Messina	312-9300
Daiquiri Deck Raw Bar	5250 Ocean Blvd	349-8697
Drunken Poet Café	1572 Main St	955-8404
El Melvin Cocina	1355 Main St	366-1618
Flavio's Brick Oven	5239 Ocean Blvd	349-0995
Gecko's Grill & Pub	6606 S Tamiami Trl	248-2020
Gecko's Grill & Pub	1900 Hillview St	953-2929
Gilligan's Island Bar	5253 Ocean Blvd	349-4759
Gulf Gate Food & Beer	6528 Superior Ave	952-3361
The Hub Baha Grill	5148 Ocean Blvd	349-6800
Irish 31	3750 S Tamiami Trl	234-9265
Island House Tap & Grl.	5110 Ocean Blvd	312-9205
JR's Old Packinghouse	987 S Packinghouse	371-9358
Made	1990 Main St	953-2900
Mandeville Beer Garden	428 N Lemon Ave	954-8688
Mattison's City Grille	1 N Lemon Ave	330-0440
Melange	1568 Main St	953-7111
Monk's Steamer Bar	6690 Superior Ave	927-3388
Munchies 420 Café	6639 Superior Ave	929-9893
Origin Beer & Pizza	3837 Hillview St	316-9222
Patrick's 1481	1481 Main St	955-1481
Pub 32	8383 S Tamiami Trl	952-3070

LATER NIGHT MENU		
Restaurant Name	**Address**	**Phone #**
Sharky's on the Pier	1600 Harbor Dr S	488-1456
Siesta Key Oyster Bar	5238 Ocean Blvd	346-5443
Walt's Fish Market	4144 S Tamiami Trl	921-4605

SARASOTA FINE & FINER DINING		
A Sprig of Thyme	1962 Hillview St	330-8890
Andrea's	2085 Siesta Dr	951-9200
Beach Bistro	6600 Gulf Dr N	778-6444
Bijou Café	1287 First St	366-8111
Café L'Europe	431 St Armands Cir	388-4415
The Crow's Nest	1968 Tarpon Ctr Dr	484-9551
Euphemia Haye	5540 Gulf of Mexico Dr	383-3633
Indigenous	239 Links Ave	706-4740
Jack Dusty	1111 Ritz-Carlton Dr	309-2266
Maison Blanche	2605 Gulf of Mexico Dr	383-8088
Melange	1568 Main St	953-7111
Michael's On East	1212 East Ave	366-0007
Ophelia's on the Bay	9105 Midnight Pass	349-2212
Pier 22	1200 1st Avenue W	748-8087
Sage	1216 1st St	445-5660
Summer House	149 Avenida Messina	206-2675

PIZZA PIE!		
Atmosphere	935 N Beneva Rd	203-8542
Baker & Wife	2157 Siesta Dr	960-1765
Bavaro's Pizza	27 Fletcher Ave	552-9131
Café Barbosso	5501 Palmer Crossing	922-7999
Café Epicure	1298 Main St	366-5648

PIZZA PIE!		
Restaurant Name	**Address**	**Phone #**
Caragiulos	69 S Palm Ave	951-0866
1592 Wood Fired Kitch	1592 Main St	365-2234
Flavio's Brick Oven	5239 Ocean Blvd	349-0995
Il Panificio	1703 Main St	366-5570
Joey D's Chicago Style	3811 Kenny Dr.	378-8900
Mattison's City Grille	1 N Lemon Ave	330-0440
Mediterraneo	1970 Main St	365-4122
Napule Ristorante	7129 S Tamiami Trl	556-9639
Oak & Stone	5405 University Pkwy	225-4590
Origin Beer & Pizza	3837 Hillview St	316-9222
Pazzo Southside	1830 S Osprey Ave	260-8831
Pizza N' Brew	1507 Main St	359-3894
Rico's Pizza - Bay Rd	1902 Bay Rd	366-8988
Ripfire Pizza & BBQ	5218 Ocean Blvd	313-7511
RomanSQ Pizza	6670 Superior Ave	237-8742
Sarasota Brewing Comp	6607 Gateway Ave	925-2337
Shaner's Pizza	6500 Superior Ave	927-2708
UPSCALE CHAIN DINING		
Bonefish Grill	3971 S Tamiami Trl	924-9090
Bravo Coastal Kitchen	3501 S Tamiami Trl	316-0868
Brio Tuscan Grille	190 Univ Town Ctr Dr	702-9102
California Pizza Kitchen	192 N Cattlemen Rd	203-6966
The Capital Grille	180 Univ Town Ctr Dr	256-3647
Fleming's Steakhouse	2001 Siesta Dr	358-9463
Kona Grill	150 Univ Town Ctr Dr	256-8005
P.F. Changs	766 S Osprey Ave	296-6002
Seasons 52	170 Univ Town Ctr Dr	702-9652

CPSIA information can be obtained
at www.ICGtesting.com
Printed in the USA
BVHW091339231221
624754BV00013B/903

9 780986 284076